D0201967

SelfCaRxe
for
HealthCare™

*Your Guide to Physical, Spiritual
and Mental Health*

By Nurse and New York Times Best Selling Author

LeAnn Thieman

Priority Publishing
Fort Collins, Colorado

Copyright 2012 LeAnn Thieman
Printed and bound in the United States of America
All rights reserved. No part of this book may be reproduced or transmitted
in any form or by any means, electronics or mechanical, including photocopying,
recording, or by an information storage and retrieval system—except by a reviewer
who may quote brief passages in a preview to be printed in a magazine,
newspaper, or on the world wide Web—without permission in writing
from the publisher. For information please contact
Priority Publishing
6600 Thompson Drive, Fort Collins CO. 80526

First printing 2012
ISBN 978-0-9727645-4-4

Although the author and publisher have made very effort to ensure the accuracy
and completeness of information contained in this book, we assume
no responsibility for errors, inaccuracies, omissions, or any inconsistencies herein.
Any slighting of people, places, or organization is unintentional.

ATTENTION CORPORATIONS, UNIVERSITIES, COLLEGES, AND
PROFESSIONAL ORGANIZATIONS: Quantity discounts are available on bulk
purchases of this book for educational or gift purposes.
Special books or book excerpts can be created to fit specific needs.
For information please contact
Priority Publishing, 6600 Thompson Drive, Fort Collins. CO 80526;
970-223-1574 www.LeAnnThieman.com or www.NurseRecruitmentandRetention.com.

Cover and book design by
Anne Vetter Graphic Design, Inc., Fort Collins, CO 80521

Welcome to SelfCare for HealthCare™

I've created this unique, fun (yes, I said fun!) program because I know what it's like to be you. As a healthcare worker, you're so busy taking care of other people that you don't always take good care of yourself. Although you may not say it out loud, you may sometimes think, "When's it my turn? When do I get time to care for me?"

The answer is... now. This book is all about—and only for—you. I promise it will help restore better health, balance, and resiliency in your life, making you a happier person.

Why twelve lessons over twelve months? For years we've heard it takes twenty-one days to change a habit and to create a new one. Now, science has proven that. We now know the brain has the ability to create new pathways (it's called neuroplasticity). Twenty-one days of reinforcing new wiring in our brains "locks in" the changes.

A key part of this program is for you to select an accountability partner, someone you will check in with at least once a month, someone with whom you will share goals, challenges, and progress. This is crucial in helping your changes "stick."

Whether you are pushing papers, pills, or brooms, you are an equally important part of the healtcare team. SelfCare for HealthCare™ is founded on a simple principle—that for caregivers to nurture the bodies, minds, and spirits of their patients, they must first nurture their own. We cannot deliver what we do not have inside.

Another bonus is that this program will help you recapture, protect, and celebrate your passion for working in healthcare. You chose this benevolent profession of caring because you have the heart of a caregiver, and these tools will reenergize your commitment to being the best caregiver possible.

So here we go, embarking on a twelve-month adventurous journey toward health and happiness...because you deserve it.

"Your Personal SelfCare Survey"

This survey is just for you. No one else needs to see it; it is simply your evaluation of your care of you today. From here you can see in what areas you need to ask for your "juice,"… your tools… to put your life into better balance. This book will guide you on your journey to take good care of you. Your turn, your time for selfcare.

1) My original hopes and goals for working in healthcare are still being fulfilled now.

     5 Always

     4 Very often

     3 Fairly often

     2 Sometimes

     1 Rarely. I'm rehearsing, "Do you want fries with that?"

2) I'm coping well with the "war zones" (challenges) of my life.

     5 Always

     4 Very often

     3 Fairly often

     2 Sometimes

     1 Rarely… Not only am I not coping in my "war zones," I need a helmet!

3) I identify stressors in my life and utilize healthy strategies for managing stress.

     5 Always

     4 Very often

     3 Fairly often

     2 Sometimes

     1 Burning out here!

4) I eat 3 healthy meals a day in appropriate quantities.

     5 Always

     4 Very often

     3 Fairly often

     2 Sometimes

     1 Hello #3 Value Meal!

5) I drink 5-6 glasses of water a day.

     5 Always

     4 Very often

     3 Fairly often

     2 Sometimes (so what am I, a camel?)

     1 Spittin' cotton

6) I get 7-8 hours of sleep in a 24 hour period.

     5 Always

     4 Very often

     3 Fairly often

     2 Sometimes

     1 Huh? Sorry I dosed off.

7) I exercise, even briefly, 5 days per week.

    5 Always

    4 Very often

    3 Fairly often

    2 Sometimes

    1 Somebody bring me the remote.

8) I breathe slow and deep 3-4 times per day, as well as in times of stress.

    5 Always

    4 Very often

    3 Fairly often

    2 Sometimes...Did you say yoga? I thought your said Yogi, as in bear.

    1 Rarely

9) I take at least 15 minute daily for relaxation.

    5 Always

    4 Very often

    3 Fairly often

    2 Sometimes ...Are you kidding me? I can barely find time to brush my teeth.

    1 Rarely...I don't floss either.

10) I laugh often and freely throughout the day.

    5 Always... Tears trickle down my pant leg!

    4 Very often

    3 Fairly often

    2 Sometimes

    1 Rarely

11) I spend time with positive, fun-loving people.

    5 Always

    4 Very often

    3 Fairly often

    2 Sometimes

    1 They're suckin' the joy right out of me!

12) I repeat positive affirmations throughout the day.

    5 Always... I am happy and hardly ever complain.

    4 Very often

    3 Fairly often

    2 Sometimes

    1 Rarely

13) I forgive people who have hurt me and I don't hold grudges.

    5 Always

    4 Very often

    3 Fairly often

    2 Sometimes

    1 I'm still mad at dead people!

14) I spend at least 15 minutes a day in quiet meditation, reflection and/or prayer.

    5 Always

    4 Very often

    3 Fairly often

    2 Sometimes

    1 Rarely... My addiction to Facebook takes all my free time.

15) I do a good job of truly living my priorities.

    5 Always… All the glass and rubber balls I'm juggling are most always in the air.

    4 Very Often

    3 Fairly often

    2 Sometimes

    1 Rarely

16) I'm satisfied with the balance between my work and home life.

    5 Completely satisfied

    4 Very satisfied

    3 Satisfied

    2 Somewhat dissatisfied

    1 Who is what's-her-name and does she live here?

17) I manage my time wisely throughout the day to accomplish my goals, balance my life, and live my priorities.

    5 Always

    4 Very often

    3 Fairly often… set the stop watch!

    2 Sometimes

    1 Rarely

18) I make good decisions, big and little.

    5 Always

    4 Very often

    3 Fairly often

    2 Sometimes… I just can't decide if I should decide.

    1 Rarely

19) I feel I'm making a good difference in the world.

     5 Completely satisfied

     4 Very satisfied

     3 Satisfied

     2 Somewhat dissatisfied

     1 Very dissatisfied. Not only am I not lighting my candle, it's burning out!

20) I have the power to choose a happier, healthier, rewarding life.

     5 Always...It's up to me.

     4 Very often

     3 Fairly often

     2 Sometimes

     1 Rarely

Total points: _____

84-100 Well balanced, happy and healthy

68-83 Mostly happy and healthy. Can use more balance in your life.

52-67 Moderately unhappy and/or unhealthy. Need to make changes to increase health and happiness.

36-51 Very unhappy and unhealthy. There's hope when you make significant changes.

20-36 Hanging on by a thread! Start SelfCare for HealthCare ASAP!

Contents

Accountability Checklist

Your accountability partner will initial this form after the completion of each month's lesson, then at the end you will be a Certified SelfCare Provider, and receive a beautiful certificate, suitable for framing!

"How Did I Get Myself into This"

One hundred little babies lay three and four to a cardboard box, strapped in the belly of a gutted C-130 cargo jet. Bombs exploded just miles away as we raced through 100-degree heat to save as many babies as possible, before Saigon fell to the communists.

With the first load of orphans on board, the American captain instructed us to prepare for takeoff, and I wondered how you prepare a hundred infants for this. Twenty-two cardboard boxes formed a row in the middle of the plane, and a long strap stretched from one end to the other, securing the boxes in place—a whole new definition of seatbelt safety. The sound of the motor was nearly deafening as the plane taxied down the runway. Its rumbling motion lulled the infants to near silence. We nine adults sat statue-like. Only the vengeful engine's roar broke the haunting, threatening stillness. Finally, the captain spoke: "We're out of range of the Vietcong. We're safe. We're going home!" Whoops of gladness and relief filled the plane. Immediately, we volunteers unfastened our seatbelts and hastened to tend to our charges.

Several large metal trashcans at the ends of the row held food, formula, and other supplies. The commotion of loading babies hadn't allowed for feeding time; now, all one hundred were awake and crying simultaneously. In a frantic effort to rehydrate as many as we could as fast as we could, we propped bottles on the shoulders of each baby's squalling box-mate. As the bottles emptied, I flung a diaper over my shoulder and burped one baby at a time with my right hand while bottle-feeding another with my left. My pediatric nursing experience prepared me for the infants' responses to stress, and soon the stuffy cargo compartment smelled of diarrhea and spit-up. The wee ones, once so neatly dressed in their homecoming outfits, now looked wrinkled and soiled. We volunteers were disheveled too, but there was merriment about it all. It was joyful work escorting babies to freedom, to families.

With one in my arms, and two in my lap, I shook my head in disbelief and shouted above the cacophony. "How did a mom and nurse get caught up in Operation Babylift?"

Ever since I was a little girl I'd been drawn to the needs of orphans. At the annual church Thanksgiving clothing drives, on the podium hung a poster of a starving child: big bloated belly, big sad eyes filled with tears. It tugged my heart. So, my seven brothers and sisters and I went home and tried on all our hand-me-down clothes. If something didn't fit Bob, Denny, Roger, Diane, Mary, Theresa, or Keith, I tried it on, since I was the runt of the litter. And if it didn't fit LeAnn, it went in the box to the needy. In retrospect, I think we were rather poor Iowa farm folk then, but I felt rich when I could give that way.

We went trick-or-treating for UNICEF every Halloween. Our teachers gathered the whole school in the gymnasium, kindergartners through twelfth grade—nearly 200 of us—and showed us film clips of Danny Kaye interacting with starving kids. Danny taught me that two and a half cents could buy a carton of milk and save a child's life. That's the first time in my life I began to believe we are called to be our brother's keeper.

We haven't been given everything we have in our lives to hoard, but to share.

I was still a little girl when I made a very important decision in my life—so important I shared it on a special day. I was only twenty when Mark and I took our romantic walk along the creek—actually, in Iowa it's called a crick. We walked on the sandbar where my sisters and I had played, and we waded in the water where my brothers had tormented me. It was there Mark asked me to marry him. As soon as I said "Yes!" I told him about my dream to adopt a child someday. From that day forward it became our dream.

Maybe it was all these things that made me stop at a bake sale booth as I strolled the mall in Iowa City in the early 1970s. I stared into the eyes of yet another starving poster child—big bloated belly, big sad eyes filled with tears. I wanted to help, to make a difference, so I picked up some cupcakes—and some cookies—and some bread—and a brochure—and learned there was a meeting the next week. Hoping I could make a simple contribution, I attended and met half a dozen young moms sitting around a chrome kitchen table with a dozen little kids running around. I learned about the cause, the needs of the orphans, and I signed on.

But my simple contribution turned into something more, when, in a few months, the chapter president moved away. I became the chapter president. Our home became the Iowa Chapter Headquarters of Friends of Children of Vietnam. This handful of women put drop boxes in grocery stores, went to doctor's offices for medications, hosted baby showers for orphans, and coordinated lots more bake sales. We raised over five tons of supplies and shipped them to Vietnam in just three years.

Attending the national conference for Friends of Children of Vietnam in Denver was a big deal for me. I'd only flown once before, and I was enthralled to meet the national officers, especially Cherie Clark, the FCVN overseas director who had come from Vietnam. I left the conference educated and bursting with excitement and enthusiasm for the difference we were making in orphanages there.

A few weeks later, I was completely blown away when the national headquarters called, asking me to be the next escort to bring six—key word here, "six"—babies to their adoptive homes in the United States.

I had twenty-four hours to decide whether I would go to Vietnam in April, 1975.

How did I ever get myself into this?

Your Turn; Your Time for SelfCare

When did you decide you wanted to work in healthcare?

Who or what influenced you the most?

Are your original hopes and goals for working in healthcare still being fulfilled now? What could change that?

What is one of your favorite patient care/work experience stories?

With your accountability partner: Choose at least one of these questions and answers to share. Bring a photo of you from when you first started in this career!

Chapter 1

"Did I Say 'Yes' to a War Zone?"

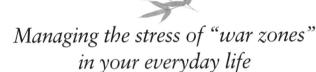

Managing the stress of "war zones" in your everyday life

When I asked Mark what he thought I should do, he said what every good husband should say when confronted with that question: "Do whatever you want to, Honey." But I knew him. Mr. Security. Mr. Stability. Mr. Safety for his family. I knew the words "Please don't go!" were screaming inside him.

I agonized over the decision. As I tossed and turned, I saw the poster child in my head, and I wanted to say, "Yes, I'll go!" I imagined Vietnam, a destitute nation, ravaged by generations of war, and its children living in impoverished conditions. The American servicemen who'd helped tremendously in the orphanages had left two years earlier. They were sorely missed as many orphanages fell into disrepair. I grieved for the fifty thousand Amerasian children (half-American, half-Asian) left behind, knowing they would never be accepted there. Completely abandoned by society, they would never have birth certificates or legal names; therefore, they could never get jobs or marry. Most Amerasian girls resorted to prostitution to support themselves and their entire ostracized families. I visualized the crippled children who received no support from the Vietnamese government, though the other orphans were allotted eleven cents per day. Everything in me wanted to go because I knew the children, the precious children, needed help and hope and health and happiness…and homes.

Although there were two dozen big reasons I wanted to say, "Yes, I'll go," there were two little reasons why I wanted to say, "No, I can't." Angela and Christie, our sweet daughters, were only two and four. They and their wonderful daddy were the number-one priorities in my life. I'd do nothing to jeopardize that.

So, how do I decide?

I considered that there had been no escalation in the war in many months. Carol, the secretary of our chapter, volunteered to go with me. She called the U.S. State Department every day, even weekends, and every day they assured her no escalation in the war was expected. We should go. We'd be safe. But mostly I considered that Mark and I had taken steps to make our dream come true. We'd applied for adoption of a son through FCVN. Although we didn't expect our little boy for two years, I knew it would mean something to him someday to know his mom had been to his homeland.

So, after much thought and a whole lot of prayer, I called Denver headquarters and said, "I'll go."

And wouldn't you know it—within a few weeks there was a terrible Vietcong offensive. Every night I sat in my living room as Walter Cronkite on the evening news presented pictures of the war raging closer and closer to the city I had promised to fly into.

I lost my courage.

I called the Denver headquarters and admitted my fears. They said I didn't have to go. Then I asked who would bring out the six babies. They answered, "Probably no one."

Again, I grieved for the lives I would mar forever if I went back on my promise.

How could something so right feel so wrong?

And why wouldn't someone ask me not to go? Then I could find the courage—not the courage to go, but the courage to stay home.

Mom mentioned the war when we talked on the phone, but she didn't say "Don't go."

My sisters called and said how hard the decision must be for me, but they didn't say "Don't go."

My brother Denny took us to dinner the week before I was to leave. Surely, he would tell me to stay home. He served in Vietnam. He lost his right arm there. But he'd seen the plight of the children. He didn't say "Don't go."

So how do you decide?

On Easter Sunday, the day before we were to leave, radio news reported bombing within three miles of Saigon. Our little family went to church as usual, but as the service ended, I found myself in turmoil, more uncertain than ever about what to do. Mark understood my unspoken need and signaled he'd take the girls downstairs for donuts.

If I stayed and prayed, surely God would say "Don't go."

Alone in the empty sanctuary, embraced by the thick sweet smell of Easter lilies, I knelt, trembling, fighting back tears. All the doubts and worries I had tried to suppress descended en masse, like a drenching rain. I felt myself crumbling. I pursed my lips together hard to keep from crying out loud, but I couldn't stop the tears trickling down my folded hands. My knees grew too weak to support me, so I sat back on the edge of the pew, put my face in my lap, and the sobs came. "What am I doing? I'm leaving everything I know and love! Please, God, give me a sign I don't have to go."

Slowly, unexpectedly, a warm feeling enveloped me, and my

tears started to subside. My breathing slowed to a calmer pace. My shoulders relaxed as an unexplainable feeling of well-being and courage filled me. I knew then, without a doubt, I was going to be okay. I was meant to go. God would take care of me.

"Thank you," was all I could manage to speak; then, I left the church, my spirits soaring!

The next day, April first, 1975, April Fools' Day now that should have been a hint!—I kissed my little girls goodbye, walked out of Mark's arms, boarded a 747, and headed for Saigon. Even the journey was difficult. We got as far as Denver, where we were greeted by the FCVN national officers, who gave Carol and me eighteen boxes of supplies to take along. No problem. But then they asked us the fateful question: Would we smuggle $10,000 in cash into Vietnam? Carol, in her wisdom, shook her head no. I listened as they explained the Vietnamese currency had no value now, whereas with ten thousand American dollars they could buy out a whole commissary and save the children's lives, so I nodded my head, yes. I made my way to the bathroom, where I created what I believe to be the most expensive padded bra in world history! I haven't checked *The Guinness Book of Records*, but I'm pretty sure I still hold that record. You've heard of Victoria's Secret? Well, this was LeAnn's secret!

We went on to California, where we were to spend the night with Carol's sister. Originally, Suzanne had been very supportive of our going to Vietnam...until she started watching Walter Cronkite too. To say she withdrew her support would be an understatement. Scared to death of losing her little sister, she spent the entire night yelling and screaming and pleading and shaming us, threatening to lock us in the bathroom to keep us from going.

I have to admit, as our plane circled Ton Son Nhut Airport, and I looked down at a runway lined with camouflaged fighter jets, Suzanne's words ran through my head, and the fear hit me again. I felt a stress I'd never known before in my life.

Dear God, I'm really in a war zone.

Certainly, we do not have to be in a war to be in a war zone. We all have versions of war zones in our everyday lives.

To begin identifying your "war zones," it helps to ponder these questions:

• What are areas of conflict in your life, personally and professionally?
• What makes you feel consistently overwhelmed and stressed?
• What things, events, or people cause you sadness and/or despair?
• What problem lurks, without an obvious solution?
• What causes you to feel incompetent and frustrated regularly?

As you examine the "war zones" facing you now, and those you've endured in the past, do you often ask, as I did in Vietnam, "Why did this happen to me? And what am I supposed to learn from or do with it?" I spent months—years, even—deciphering that. As unlikely as it may sound, I realized that "war zones" in our lives today are a lot like those I experienced in Vietnam.

Having too much to do and not enough time and resources to get it all done.

Being given big assignments and not enough support to do it right.

Trying so hard to do it right, but feeling sometimes like we're working with one hand tied behind our backs.

Giving 100%—some days 110%—but knowing it isn't enough. No matter what we do, it's never enough.

Feeling torn between work and family and volunteerism.

Having too many people all counting on us and feeling like we can't do it all.

Being so busy taking care of everybody else, we have little time to care for ourselves.

Does some of this sound too familiar? Because our personal "war zones" today are so similar to mine in Vietnam, the lessons I learned there apply.

Do you ever feel like I did then—like you don't have enough support to do it all?

When no one asked me not to go—not my mother, my sisters, my brother, my husband, not even God—I assumed they were stifling their objections. I caution you not to make the mistake I did. It wasn't until I spent years sorting all this out that I realized they didn't ask me not to go because, as Mark later said, they believed in me. They knew I could do it even when I did not. It wasn't a silent objection they felt, but silent support. I suggest that you, too, have more silent supporters in your life than you realize.

But even with support, do you sometimes feel like I did? Too weak, too tired, too afraid, too confused to keep it all up? To cope, we have to be strong in mind, body, and spirit, and we must make choices to ensure that.

Yet too often, we are so devoted to caring for our patients, families, friends, and even strangers that we neglect to care for ourselves. This demand leaves us depleted physically, mentally, and spiritually, often without our even realizing it. This list of symptoms helps identify the toll that stress takes on your mind, body, and spirit:

Symptoms of Stress

PHYSICAL	MENTAL	SPIRITUAL
Appetite changes	Forgetfulness	Emptiness
Headaches	Poor concentration	Loss of meaning
Fatigue	Dull senses	Doubt
Poor sleeping	Lethargy	Martyrdom
Frequent illnesses	Boredom	Loss of direction
Digestive problems	Low productivity	Cynicism
Pounding heart	Negative attitude	Apathy
Teeth grinding	Anxiety	Abandonment
Rash	The "blues"	Worry
Restlessness	Mood swings	Isolation
Foot-tapping	Anger	Distrust
Finger drumming	Bad dreams	"No one cares"
Smoking	Irritability	
Increased alcohol intake	Crying spells	
	Nervous laughter	
	Loss of loving feeling	

Whether you identified two or twenty of these symptoms, you'll benefit from:

Ways to Reduce Stress

First, identify the triggers. Although you can't jump to the head of the line at the grocery store or wish the traffic jam away or convince your husband to clean up his kitchen mess, you can control how you react to these situations.

Eliminate or delegate some of the activities that consume your time.Reduce the noise around you. Turn down or shut off televisions, radios, or rowdy kids.

Avoid rushing. Leave sooner. Get up earlier.

Plan ahead. Don't let the gas tank get below one-fourth full. Keep staples stocked in the kitchen. Don't wait until you use your last bus token or postage stamp to buy more, etc.

Stay healthy. Eat, sleep, exercise so you are strong and can manage better.

Stay positive. Keep away from grumpy negative people. Choose positive affirmations and people.

Pray and meditate every day.

Repair or replace things that don't work properly (family members not included).

Don't rely on your memory. Write things down.

Break big tasks into bite-sized manageable portions.

Un-clutter and organize, so you can easily find things.

Simplify, simplify, simplify.

Quit trying to "fix" other people.

Lower your standards and expectations. Some things aren't worth doing perfectly. Shoot for sevens—we can't always score a ten.

Okay, once you've reduced it as much as you can, here are ways to cope with the remaining stress:

There's no reason to be stretched to the breaking point in your everyday life. Regain control of how you respond to the stress of your "war zones."

Ways to Cope with Stress

Smile, even if you don't feel like it, and hold it for thirty seconds. Smiling releases endorphins, giving you calm and control.

Do relaxation breathing and visualization exercises.

Visualize yourself responding to the stressor in a calm, empowered manner.

Take a time out. Pop in a CD that provides relaxation, humor, or easy listening music.

Exercise. At work, find a stairwell. Or put a file under your arm and walk quickly on your "urgent assignment."

Get outdoors. Walk. Fresh air and nature's breezes help blow stress away.

Pray. My mom sent me a greeting card that read: "God helps us in times of stress, to live at our magnificent best."

Eat right. Add extra protein for more energy.

Sleep. Too often we deprive ourselves of sleep during stressful times, yet it is a critical recovery tool.

Sing. When dealing with stress-related problems, African shamans ask, "When did you stop singing?"

Share your feelings with others or in a journal.

Your Turn; Your Time for SelfCare

Based on the questions on page 17, what are the war zones in your life?

Pause to consider, who are your silent supporters?

List three things that cause you stress.

Review the Symptoms of Stress on page 19.
List the physical symptoms of stress that apply to you.

List the mental symptoms of stress that apply to you.

List the spiritual symptoms of stress that apply to you.

What specific steps will you take to avoid them?

Choose one of the Ways to Reduce Stress you will implement this week. Then choose one for the next week. And the next.

Choose one of the "Ways to Cope with Stress" you will you practice this week. Then choose one for the next week. And the next.

With your accountability partner: Compare how you felt before you eliminated or reduced a stressor to how you felt after. Do you want that to be a consistent practice? What steps will you take to continue this practice?

Chapter 2

"Am I Strong Enough to Do This?"

Balancing your life physically

Shaking, I descended the plane's steps and walked across that sun-baked tarmac, heading for the customs counter. I glanced down to check my chest, my heart beating heavily under all the cash. In Denver, the FCVN national officers had told me to keep quiet and "just act natural." There was nothing natural about this. They'd also told us we could buy anything or anyone in Vietnam, even our way through customs.

Mean-looking Vietnamese guards with enormous guns glared at Carol and me. If the John Wayne World War II movies I'd seen were any indication, these were the bad guys. I shivered with fear as one waved his gun to motion me into line. I gripped the bare grimy two-by-fours, stained by thousands of sweaty hands before us, and hoped my blouse wasn't quaking with the thumping of my heart. Trembling and panting, I worried, *Will that guard take one look at this bodacious bosom and know this was not an act of God? Will he frisk me, find the money, and throw me into prison? Will I ever see Mark and my girls again?*

"Di chuyen!" he barked. I jumped. My mind raced, grasping for something to calm me down before I gave myself away. I conjured up all the positive thinking I'd ever learned, every positive visualization I'd ever seen, every prayer I'd ever recited. Then, I remembered the relaxation breathing I'd learned in my childbirth classes. The instructor said it was a life skill, not just a labor skill.

It worked then; will it work now? "In-two-three-four, out-two-three-four. In-two-three-four, out two-three-four," I breathed. Then I looked down at my huge heaving chest and realized I was counting, "In one thousand, two thousand, three thousand *dollars* and out four thousand, five thousand, six thousand *dollars*."

My own laughter released my tension but apparently annoyed the guards. I wiped the smirk off my face and with steady hands lifted my bag onto the counter. The soldier scowled and gestured at the eighteen boxes already stacked there. "What you have inside?" he demanded.

"Documents and supplies," I said as calmly as I could. He didn't seem to understand. So, I shouted, "Documents and supplies!" Surely he could interpret the language better if I said it louder. The soldier muttered over the bags and boxes for another minute, then raised his gun. I willed myself not to gasp or clutch my chest. His weapon pointed toward me...then waved me on. I couldn't believe it. That was it! We were clear and out of danger...for now, at least. Carol and I picked up our bags and headed out before he could change his mind.

"LeAnn! LeAnn!" a voice called. I turned to see Cherie, the overseas director I'd met at the conference in Denver. I rushed to hug her, then stepped back and noticed her small frame looked worn and frazzled, as though she hadn't slept in days. "Did you hear the news?" Her haggard face lit up with excitement. I realized then that we'd been traveling for over twenty-four hours and had no exposure to television, radio, or newspapers. "President Ford has okayed a giant baby lift! Instead of taking out six babies, you'll help take out three hundred if we're lucky!"

"Three hundred babies? Three hundred babies?" My mind

could hardly grasp it. It was then that I knew why I had said yes, what was driving me to go. This mission was bigger than I could possibly have imagined.

Chattering with excitement, Carol and I helped Cherie pack the eighteen boxes into her Volkswagen. No, not a van. A Bug, a VW Beetle. With bags and boxes tied to the top, strapped on the back, and jammed in the trunk, Carol and I crammed into the front bucket seat, and Cherie maneuvered us through the overcrowded, chaotic streets of Saigon. Two-lane streets were jammed with eight lanes of traffic...hundreds of cars, thousands of bicycles and motorbikes and pushcarts loaded with people and seemingly all their possessions. Horns honked, tires screeched, and people yelled as our car veered through the congestion. Street vendors lined the sidewalks, selling uncovered meats and vegetables. Smells of fresh fish and fowl permeated the hot, humid air. I winced, watching flies swarm around plucked chicken carcasses hanging from a wire rack, their heads and feet still intact.

Then, there, in the middle of the street I saw a sandbag fortress with a Vietnamese soldier peering over the top, pointing a gun. A stark realization: *This country is at war.*

Even the deafening noises were unfamiliar to me as thousands of Saigonese shouted to one another and bicycles and motorbikes buzzed past our overloaded VW. Men and women alike carried yokes on their shoulders with baskets or bags at both ends. I felt like I was part of a picture from *National Geographic.* Some buildings of tin and shabby wood seemed barely strong enough to stand. Others were modern and resembled those of concrete and brick in the States.

"This isn't the best part of the city. You should see the magnificent buildings and houses and beautiful beaches and palm trees," Cherie said with obvious pride. "Vietnam is like an island paradise."

We turned onto a quiet narrower side street, lined with ramshackle buildings, and eventually through the black, cast-iron gates of the FCVN Orphanage Center. Palm trees and flowers surrounded the circle drive. The two-story structure, made of smooth white stone with wrought-iron verandas, looked like a mansion in Europe—a bit of elegance in the midst of squalor.

Our car halted in the driveway, and immediately Vietnamese workers came to help unload the eighteen boxes.

Inside, I was thrilled to see Sister Terese, a Catholic nun I had met at the FCVN convention in Denver. Unlike the nuns I had known as a youngster, she didn't wear a habit, but sported casual dress, wavy brown hair, and a lighthearted smile.

Her face blanched, and her jaw dropped when I reached into my shirt and pulled out $10,000! "My Mom always said I should pin some cash to my bra for emergency money when I travel," I quipped. Everyone laughed as Cherie placed the cash in the huge black safe sitting in the corner. She praised me for the risk I had taken and told us about the lifesaving supplies she could buy.

Just then, a young man in his early twenties with unkempt curly brown hair, a bushy mustache, and sweat-stained clothes came bounding in. "Hi, I'm Ross." He pumped our hands and pushed his glasses back onto the bridge of his nose. I liked him immediately.

"Let's show you around," Cherie said as she pushed open a wooden door leading to the nursery.

Although I was a nurse working in pediatrics, nothing in my life had prepared me for what I was about to witness and be a part of. The center that usually held ten babies, too sick to be in foster homes, now held nearly one hundred!

Babies were coming from FCVN's foster homes, other orphanages, and care centers in preparation for the airlift. Every inch of nursery floor was covered with a mat, and every inch of mat was covered with a baby. Seas and seas of babbling, burping, bawling babies. Some looked beautifully healthy, others sickly. Nursery smells of wet and dirty diapers, spit-up, baby powder, and formula multiplied tenfold in the hot, humid, yet meticulously clean room. A wide staircase took us to the next level, where the noise grew louder as dozens more babies lay close together on bright-colored woven mats and sheets. I watched a worker slowly and tenderly feed a baby girl in an infant seat, her top lip deformed by a cleft palate. I recalled how these babies and their families were ostracized because ancient tradition suggested demons were the cause. I smiled, knowing an American family and physician could heal her.

When we went back downstairs, I gestured to a worker that I wanted to feed a baby. She nodded and handed me the one in her arms.

"Carol, take my picture," I beamed, and she took the first photo of me in Vietnam. As I spent the rest of that day feeding, diapering, and rocking scores of babies, I knew...somehow I was on assignment.

Finally, late at night Carol and I fell into bed, exhausted. I'd never felt so physically depleted. *Will I be strong enough to do this?*

To cope in our war zones and even our everyday lives and activities, we must be strong in body, mind, and spirit. In this chapter we'll explore ways to take better care of our bodies.

Diet

Most of us think we are eating better than we actually are. When I wrote down everything I ate for a week, I was surprised to read what I'd consumed. Too often, if my Wendy's hamburger didn't have lettuce on it, I didn't get any vegetables that day.

Volumes are written on healthy diets, but the subject doesn't have to be so complicated. Here is a nutshell version to get you started:

The United Nations Food and Agricultural Organization released a report stating diet-related chronic illnesses are responsible for nearly 60 percent of all deaths. In the U.S., 1.3 million people die each year from self-inflicted diet-related diseases. If such a toll were inflicted by a new virus, we would mobilize all our health resources and impose a national quarantine!

Healthy Eating, in a Nutshell

6–8 servings of whole grains per day. Make sure the label says "whole wheat," not refined "white flour," as it's unhealthy. Rice, corn, beans, and oatmeal are good.

3 servings of vegetables

3 servings of fruit

3 servings of low-fat milk products (or calcium-fortified soy products)

2 servings lean meat. Eat seafood twice a week

No trans fats, no hydrogenated or partially-hydrogenated oils. (Most fast foods are fried in these oils.)

Avoid saturated fats. Use olive oil and canola.

ChooseMyPlate.gov

Not only do we forget to eat right, but we also forget to drink— water, that is. We've all read about the importance of drinking two quarts of water a day. How simple is that? Yet how often do you remember to do it? Seventy-five percent of Americans are chronically dehydrated, causing daytime fatigue, memory impairment, difficulty focusing, headaches, nausea, and poor metabolism. Research shows that drinking five glasses of water a day decreases colon, breast, and bladder cancers.

To get your recommended amount of water daily, try filling up a container or water bottle to consume throughout the day. Another tip is to drink a glass of water each time you go to the bathroom. Make a plan to drink a healthy amount of water; it's easy.

Sleep

More and more research is proving the importance of sleep. The National Sleep Foundation estimates two out of three people are sleep-deprived.

Although teenagers need eight to nine hours of sleep, only 15 percent of them actually get it.

Grownups aren't the only ones affected by this increasing problem. A study in Japan proved that children who got fewer than ten hours of sleep a night were significantly more likely to be obese.

Another study of more than a thousand patients found that overweight people sleep less than lean ones. When we sleep, a hormone called leptin rises in our systems. Leptin controls our appetites. The higher our leptin levels, the less hungry we are. Poor sleep seems to interrupt leptin's rise, so those who don't get enough sleep tend to be hungrier. Have you noticed that when you are over-tired, you feel more hungry? I still remember getting off 11 to 7 shifts feeling starved until I got some sleep.

Nearly 60 percent of motor vehicle accidents—that's 100,000 per year—are related to sleepy drivers. Sixty-six percent of men and 49 percent of women admit to driving while drowsy, and 23 percent say they've fallen asleep at the wheel in the past year.

Sleep studies show that we experience two intervals of increased sleepiness and low performance in a twenty-four-hour period. One is from midnight to 6 A.M., and the other occurs in the mid-afternoon, around 2 to 4 P.M. That explains why my head is nodding at the computer at that time of day. Maybe we should do as many other societies throughout the world do and take an afternoon rest and nap time. Even fifteen to twenty minutes helps. Studies show our bodies are really geared to do that, but we just ignore it.

For Better Sleep

Keep regular bedtime hours.

Avoid alcohol and coffee later in the day. (Alcohol may help put you to sleep but actually disrupts your sleep during the night.)

Don't eat for two hours before bedtime.

Develop stress management techniques.

Complete work early so you don't take stress to bed.

Exercise regularly but not just before sleep time.

Practice meditation and relaxation techniques.

Make sure your bedroom is conducive to a good night's sleep. Keep it dark, quiet, and cool, with no pets on the bed to lick your face or take your space.

If you wake up in the middle of the night, do rhythmic breathing (chapter 3).

Don't toss and turn. If you can't go back to sleep, get out of bed and go to a relaxing area to read until you become sleepy again.

Restore lost sleep as soon as possible. A power nap works wonders.

Nearly 50 percent of men and women in America say they would go to bed earlier if they didn't watch TV or have Internet access. These technologies provide a perfect opportunity for you to use some good decision-making skills and practice good sleep hygiene.

Seven out of ten Americans say they experience frequent sleep problems. Scientists have found that when sleep is inadequate, health deteriorates, resulting in lowered glucose tolerance, impaired thyroid function, fatigue, increased heart rate, decreased strength, increased blood pressure, stomach and bowel problems, pain, and decreased abilities to fight disease.

For a safer, healthier life, says the National Sleep Foundation, get a good night's sleep and learn to enjoy a guilt-free siesta. Tell your boss I said so.

In kindergarten, our teacher made us lie down or put our heads on our desks and just rest for a while. I think Mrs. Geltz had something there.

Exercise

Regular exercise is essential to nurture our bodies physically. But that's a hard discipline for me. I don't like mundane exercise routines or gyms. I don't enjoy exercising those ways, so I don't do it. That's why I appreciate research proving thirty to forty minutes of brisk walking, three or four times a week, has the same cardiovascular benefit as jogging. I imagine all the runners with the bad knees resent this information coming out now, but it sure works better for me. Even on my busiest days, I can usually get in a thirty-minute walk. Just fifteen minutes of walking or exercise is beneficial because the results are cumulative. A recent study shows that the best way to boost metabolism is with moderate short exercises throughout the day. Taking the stairs, parking far away from your destination, and walking to the store all count.

Burn 100 calories	*Burn 200 calories*
26 minutes vacuuming	40 minutes playing badminton
29 minutes washing windows	30 minutes chasing toddler on beach
18 minutes scrubbing floors	60 minutes miniature golf
30 minutes searching for seashells on a beach	60 minutes dancing cheek to cheek

Even if you don't plant an acre of garden and dig potatoes like Grandma, you can get a great workout gardening and doing yard work. Squatting strengthens your leg muscles, makes your thighs fit and firm, builds your muscles in your back, and slims your waist. Spading strengthens your biceps, triceps, legs, and chest muscles. Raking works the upper back, biceps, and triceps. Pushing a loaded wheelbarrow uses almost every muscle in your body. (I'll attest to that!) Besides, fresh air is good for the lungs, heart, and spirit.

A great life balance tool is to incorporate exercise into the priorities and assignments of your life. If your partner is a priority, you can enjoy sports and outdoor activities together or go dancing, a great form of exercise, and you get to hold each other too! If community service is a priority, you can get good exercise lifting boxes at the food distribution center or painting a house for Habitat for Humanity. If a priority is caring for family, you can get a lot of exercise with your sweetheart or your kids by biking, walking, hiking, swimming, or simply playing ball in the backyard.

Exercising with your children boosts their self-esteem, improves their endurance, and lays foundations for lifelong fitness. You help them become more fit, and you too, while building a closer relationship.

It's estimated that the average child in America spends seven to eight hours a day on "screen time," such as computers, video games, and the Internet. Seven hours a day for seven days a week is 49 hours, which is more than most people spend on a full-time job! To worsen the situation, physical education classes in schools are becoming fewer and shorter. Some are even offered online. Now there's a real calorie burner!

Recent government reports say one-third of U.S. children are overweight. Obesity increases a child's risk of developing serious illnesses such as type 2 diabetes.

Start a new fitness tradition with your kids. For example, reserve Sunday evenings for after-dinner walks or weekend mornings for biking. You might run while your preschooler rides his tricycle or bicycle. In no time at all, these rituals will become the highlight of your week and theirs. Try this rule: For every hour of television you or your child watches, schedule an hour of physical activity.

Plan a family vacation, perhaps a camping trip, skiing holiday, or canoeing adventure. In preparation, you can train and get in shape together. As a grownup, you'll rediscover the joy of tag and other childhood games. You are sure to feel young again after a rousing game of Duck Duck Goose.

At one of my seminars a young mom shared her best way of combining exercise with assignments and priorities. She said that as soon as her kids get off of the school bus, she—and her husband if he is home too—walk around the cul-de-sac with them while they talk about their days. This ritual gives their whole family a lot more than just exercise, doesn't it? It says to the kids: You are most important to me, and I can hardly wait for you to get home so we can all do this together.

Exercise not only lowers your risk of heart attacks, diabetes, bone cancer, osteoporosis, arthritis, backaches, high blood pressure, depression, and stress, but it can also increase your family's health and happiness too.

It's time to care for yourself as consciously as you do others— time to give your body the nutrition, sleep, and exercise it needs.

You deserve it.

Your Turn; Your Time for SelfCare

Keep a dietary log for one week. Based on it, what modifications from the "Healthy Eating" list will you make to your diet?

What plan will you implement to drink five glasses of water per day?

Are you getting the required seven to eight hours of sleep in a twenty-four-hour period? If not, what specific things are preventing you? What will you change? (See www.sleepfoundation.org for more information and tips if needed.)

What three things will you implement from the suggestions "For Better Sleep"?

Is there a time when you can schedule a fifteen-minute power-nap? When?

Are you getting exercise on a daily/weekly basis? What specific steps will you take to increase your exercise?

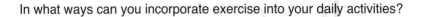

In what ways can you incorporate exercise into your daily activities?

If you are a 'beginner," when can you schedule fifteen minutes per day, every day for exercise?

With your accountability partner: Choose one step you will take this month to improve your diet, your sleep, and your exercise.

Chapter 3

"In All This Commotion I Can't Hear Myself Think!"

Balancing your life mentally with breathing and relaxation

Bam! Bam! Bam! The exploding sounds sent Carol and me upright in bed. Fear stole my breath. "What was that?" I heard a motorcycle drive away. "Maybe just backfire from that motorbike." Six more blasts jolted us into each other's arms. "That's gunfire! Oh, God! It is the war! The city is being invaded!"

For the first time since I had left my little girls, the thought ravaged my mind: *I might never see my family again. I might die here.*

What should I do? I can't just sit here and wait for soldiers to come charging up the stairs. I slithered out of bed, then crawled on my belly to the veranda. Cautiously, I peered over the railing, fearing my head could be blown off as I peeked over the ledge. The center's yard lamp lit up the street below. There was no sign of activity. Crickets chirped.

Still ducking down, I snuck back to Carol. "Maybe soldiers are already inside. We better go downstairs and see what's going on." We approached the steps, my mind and heart racing with fear. *What if the soldiers are in the office? What if they have Cherie? Will they take us prisoners too? Will I ever see my family*

*again? Maybe I should have just stayed hidden in the bedroom.
That would be pretty cowardly, with our fellow workers being
held captive.*

We tiptoed down the steps, gripping the handrail, trying not
to let our labored breaths be heard. *How can the workers sleep
when the place is under communist siege?* Slowly, we opened the
door to the office, where Sister Terese sat typing. She looked up,
nonchalantly. "Why aren't you asleep?"

"We heard gunshots! We thought the war was here!"

"Oh," she smiled knowingly, "they draft twelve-year-olds
in Vietnam. It was just the young boy-soldiers entertaining
themselves during the night by shooting at rats, signs, and such."

"No communists?"

She shook her head. "No communists."

"Oh. Never mind." With that, I went back to bed for a fitful
night's sleep.

The next morning at breakfast, Ross teased me about the
"invasion." I joked along and recounted the hilarity of our actions,
each time dramatizing it a bit more. I admitted my foolishness—
and lingering fear. Then, jovially, we began a full day of caring.

That evening, Cherie was delighted to announce she'd made
arrangements for us to dine at the American Officers' Club, a
special treat from her to us. We tried to coax her to join us, but
she refused to leave her office and airlift preparations. There was
no word about when we were to leave, but she wanted to be
ready when it came. Ross, Carol, and I admitted we felt a little
guilty, leaving to have fun while she continued to work.

There was a spirit of festivity in the bar, a stark wooden-
paneled room filled with wooden tables and chairs. We found
another American, Steve, sitting at the long table. He smiled
proudly as he nodded toward his Vietnamese wife singing on the

small stage at the end of the room. The pianist swayed to her emotion while accompanying her on the old upright piano as she sang a sad American melody. Her straight black hair flowed over the shoulders of her shapely body as she crooned the lonely song. She joined us at the table and sat next to Steve, who looked like an "all American boy" with sandy brown hair and a slim build. His light blue, deep-set eyes reflected sorrow as he told us about his plan to send his sons to his parents in the States with us on the airlift while he stayed behind to arrange passage for his wife— a difficult endeavor since she was a Vietnamese citizen.

She drank her full glass of wine quickly and returned to the stage. But the wine couldn't ease the obvious pain she felt at the prospect of saying goodbye to her little boys. Her tears flowed as she sang another melancholy tune. I thought of the pain I felt when I said goodbye to my girls a few days earlier. I couldn't imagine the agony she felt, not knowing when she'd be with her sons again.

An American dinner of baked potatoes, steak, and salad was served. Carol reminded me of the warnings others had given us en route not to eat fresh fruits and vegetables. Ross assured us, however, that all the food was brought from the United States and would be safe. I, in my usual naive trusting way, enjoyed the greens. Carol, in her usual cautious manner, declined.

Since I had eaten very little for two days, the food tasted good, and in spite of the sadness, we talked and teased each other lightheartedly. Still, the cloud of worry about the approaching war cast a shadow on the fun.

"It's real close" is all Steve would say. The tortured look on his wife's face confirmed that fact. For an instant we all sat in an uncomfortable, solemn silence. Then, in an apparent attempt to change the mood, she went back on stage and bellowed out

"Won't You Come Home Bill Bailey" in her throatiest voice. We all clapped and howled. Ross put his fingers to his lips in a shrieking whistle.

"It's hard to believe we're in Vietnam," I shouted above the music. This was a scene out of America.

But the reality of the war returned as Ross warned, "We need to leave now if we're to get back by the ten o'clock curfew."

Abruptly, the festivities ended, and Ross drove fast through the nearly abandoned streets.

"Even the toughest street boys, prostitutes, and soup vendors get off the streets an hour before deadline. They're all afraid of the communists."

We arrived at the center to find it filled with more than one hundred babies now and dozens of workers. There were only two bathrooms in the building, and I excused myself and raced to the closest one, where I experienced abdominal cramping and explosive diarrhea. Everyone else prepared for bed as I grew more ill. I started to dress for bed, but rushed immediately back to the bathroom. It was occupied, so I ran to the one upstairs, which was also being used. The abdominal pain increased as I lay on the floor outside the door, feeling like my bowels would burst. The occupant must have heard my moaning and quickly exited. I entered the bathroom for what would be one of many times that night.

With my sweater under my head for a pillow, I slept fitfully on the office floor. The increasing agony in my belly woke me, and I ran to the toilet over and over again, scurrying quietly past the sleeping workers and babies. When both bathrooms were occupied, I collapsed on the floor outside the door. The cool tile soothed my burning face as I drifted in and out of sleep. The pains increased, like childbirth. I curled up in a ball and tried not to moan out loud as I breathed, just like when I was in labor with our daughters.

Have you ever felt as physically and mentally depleted as I did in Vietnam, wondering if you can cope? We can manage better in our "war zones" when we use four mental balance tools. The first is:

Breathing

Deep relaxation breathing is one of the best and most effective tools for mental rest, relaxation, and focus, but it is so simple that most people don't appreciate its value. It relieves stress and tension and releases endorphins, our bodies' own pain medication.

I was a childbirth educator for thirteen years, and I taught moms to breathe slowly, deeply, and easily to reduce stress and pain in labor. The same principles apply as we "labor" through life.

When laboring women get too stressed, they experience increased adrenaline, which shuts down the release of oxytocin, the hormone that makes the uterus contract and the baby come out. Too much adrenaline from too much stress makes for a longer, harder labor.

Stress raises adrenaline levels in all of us, putting us into the "fight or flight mode," an ancient survival mechanism left over from when cavemen were chased by wild beasts. In this mode, our bodies send all the energy and circulation to the organs needed at that moment and take energy away from those not needed for survival then. That's why our hearts beat so fast and our breathing is rapid

Relaxation Breathing

Three or four times a day, for three to four minutes at a time, simply breathe in (two-three-four), out (two-three-four). The breaths should be slow, deep, and easy from your abdomen. Imagine a hot air balloon expanding in your chest with each breath, then deflating as you exhale. Breathe in a relaxing pace you could keep up for hours, never feeling short of breath. Breaths will grow deeper as you continue. You can add a thought with each, perhaps breathing in thinking, "I am-two-three four" and out "relaxed-two-three-four."

when we get scared. We need a heartbeat and breathing to survive. What we don't need is a bladder. That's why kindergarteners wet their pants on stage. They are so nervous up there, trying to sing their songs, that their little hearts and lungs are working overtime to help them survive.

This is also why the bride has to go to the bathroom just one more time before she walks down the aisle and why guys at work have to duck into the men's room before talking to the supervisor. Think of the last time you were really nervous and afraid. Did you have to go to the bathroom?

You've likely read stories of heroes in a "fight or flight mode" lifting a car off the injured victim, proving that adrenaline kicks in to help the organs needed to survive. Too much adrenaline, however, interrupts healthy body function.

Breathing and relaxing decrease adrenaline output and allow all of our organs and body parts to work at their best and "save" us.

A lot of activities, not just rhythmic breathing, release endorphins: walking, biking, swimming, laughing, dancing, crying, jogging. Endorphins can even become addictive. Do you know runners who cannot miss a day? I have a friend who is so used to that endorphin release that if it is raining or hailing, she is inside on her stationary bike to get her rhythmic endorphin "fix." Many runners tell me that after they jog so far, they feel a surge, a second wind that pushes them on. That's the endorphins, the "morphine," our body's built-in painkillers kicking in.

I learned a lot from teaching my childbirth classes. One participant worked with those who were severely physically and mentally handicapped. He said, "Haven't you ever noticed how sometimes those individuals rock? They have the same innate survival skills we were all born with but we trained ourselves out of. They know rhythmic rocking brings comfort." A gerontologist in class piped up and concurred, "That's why old people rock. They revert back to those innate survival senses." A neonatal nurse offered, "That's why babies quit crying when you rock them."

I think we have a lot to learn from these people and crying babies. Let's breathe slowly, deeply, and easily three to four times a day for three to four minutes and relax.

Robert Louis Stevenson said, "Quiet minds cannot be perplexed or frightened, but go on in fortune at their own private pace, like the ticking of a clock during a thunderstorm."

Relaxation breathing is even more effective when we combine it with:

Relaxation

We schedule so many activities into our days; we should also schedule relaxation. Ideally, we should allocate at least fifteen minutes a day for deep breathing and relaxation, which can also be combined with meditation or prayer. When we do, it becomes a habit, and we can tap into those feelings all day long.

Studies at Loma Linda University proved that music reduces stress, whether from illness, home, or the workplace. The rhythmic beat of music releases endorphins and relieves pain.

Relaxation can be enhanced by adding music. Many people find that music with the four-four beat makes their hearts beat to that time and will eventually slow to sixty beats per minute, the same as the music Listening to it often makes relaxation instantaneous.

When researchers added videos blending music, scenic imagery, and positive statements to relaxation exercises, they found it reduced levels of hormones that suppress the immune system. They drew blood before and after the videos and noted a 20 percent decrease in hormone levels.

Keeping our bodies relaxed keeps our emotions under control. We are only as relaxed as our hands and our face. We can't relax if we're making a fist or clenching our teeth or the steering wheel. It took me a long time to realize that I didn't get through a traffic jam any faster when I gritted my teeth or pounded the steering wheel. When I popped in a CD of relaxation music and did my deep breathing, I got there in the same amount of time and in a much better mood. Isn't the road rage phenomenon unfathomable? We need to uncurl our fists, decrease our anger, breathe deeply, and relax.

Relaxation Exercise

Sag back in your chair. Start relaxing every muscle, beginning with your toes. Stretch out your legs, flex your ankles, try to push your toes right off your feet, then let everything go limp. Let your head fall back. Roll it around so your neck muscles loosen up. Let each hand fall on your knees and rest there as limp as a wet leaf on a log. Open your eyes wide, then pretend invisible weights are attached to your eyelids, slowly pulling them shut. Imagine a soft gentle hand lightly touching your face, smoothing the tension lines away. Picture the tension draining out of your body, leaving it calm and peaceful and relaxed.

Now see yourself alone in your favorite forest on a perfect summer's day. You are sitting with your back against a tree; your can feel the rough bark through your shirt. All around you is a forest of fir, spruce, and evergreen. The air is scented with balsam.

You can hear the gentle sighing in the treetops as birds and crickets chirp. That breeze brushes against your face and cools it. In the far distance, green hills are outlined against a tranquil blue heaven. The sky is mirrored in the gleaming mountain stream gently rolling beside you, babbling along smooth, glistening rocks. The warm sun falls on your face like a benediction.

Now visualize that sun warming your body, ever so slowly from your toes toward your head. The warmth is slowly moving from your legs, over your hips, past your stomach. The warm feeling of relaxation is now entering your chest. As it does, concentrate on your breathing. Breathing in ever so slowly, and breathing out. As you breathe in, you are breathing in rays of energy and comfort. Feel the warmth of these rays as they enter your lungs and radiate warmth throughout your body and relax you. As you breathe in, think slowly to yourself "I am," and as you breathe out, think "relaxed." "I am relaxed; I am relaxed."

Feel that relaxation spread from your chest to your shoulders and down your arms toward your fingertips. You may feel some tingling sensations in your hands or feet or down your spine. That's okay—it's just the discharge of nervous energy as you become more and more relaxed.

Now that total relaxation has been achieved, visualize that bright, energizing sun above your head. Feel the warmth from the rays covering and immersing your body in a blanket of warmth. The sun's rays are drawing from you all of your tensions and thoughts. The day's hassles, problems, and worries are leaving you now, and your mind is clear and at peace. Everything about you and everything around you feels good. Your whole body from your head to your toes is now engulfed in these magical golden rays of sun. You feel warm, soothed, and relaxed. Totally at peace and comfortable. Your breathing is slow and deep. Your face is calm and expressionless. You are relaxed. You are calm. You feel wonderful.

Look around at the sights and hear the sounds of your relaxation place. Get to know it well, for once you have created your visualization, the trip back will not be as time consuming and may become instantaneous. Take time now to feel the sun, to hear the soothing songs of the birds and the rippling stream as you relax.

Your Turn; Your Time for SelfCare

What occasion has caused you to feel stressed or afraid and made your heart race? (That was the adrenaline at work!)

What situation is a good time for you to use rhythmic breathing to help you cope?

What fantastic stories have you heard of people accomplishing feats of super-human strength when their bodies were in "fight or flight mode"?

List four times a day you will spend three to four minutes doing deep rhythmic relaxation breathing.

Look at your daily schedule. When can you write in a time to do your fifteen-minute relaxation exercise?

Spend the rest of your time on this lesson, practicing your breathing and relaxation.

With your accountability partner: Describe if and how relaxation has helped you reduce stress. How did it work? What got in the way? What can you do to make it even more effective?

Chapter 4

"You're Joking, Right?"

Balancing your life mentally with laughter

At breakfast the next morning, as we ate fresh baked bread and drank cola (the only things that seemed "safe" to eat by then), Cherie gave Carol and me our assignment for the day: pack for three hundred kids.

We walked to the two-story warehouse behind the center and looked around at the rows and rows of well-organized shelves and labeled boxes. Pulling a cardboard box from a stack, I laughed. "How do we begin to find six hundred sleepers and one thousand disposable diapers?"

I pulled another labeled box from its place, brushed dust from the lid, and gasped. "Can you believe this? This is my handwriting! We sent this from my basement last month!" The significance of the work we'd been doing in Iowa City became a reality. All the efforts, all the slide shows, all the volunteer hours had been worth it.

We sorted through the shirts, pants, and playsuits we recognized, delighting in the fact that the clothes would return to the States, this time on an infant going home. For hours we worked, separating clothes by size and gathering items needed for the trip.

"They're watching *Sesame Street*," I murmured.

"What?"

"Angela and Christie are watching *Sesame Street* now. I

keep my watch on Iowa time so I know what they're doing while I'm here."

I choked up as I thought of them. I missed them so much.

It grew increasingly hotter inside the metal building, and the air became polluted with mouse excrement and dirt we stirred up. By noon, the lack of an adequate breakfast took its toll, and I admitted feeling faint.

"What we need is a sugar boost." I recalled the jellybeans I had confiscated before filling Angela's and Christie's Easter baskets. Carol admitted that she too was not feeling well, so I made my way to the center and my flight bag to retrieve the candies. When I returned, I found Carol with her head resting on a grimy box, looking quite pale.

"Here, these will help," I said in a soothing voice and handed her a fistful of assorted jellybeans.

Carol whined ever so slightly, "I only like orange ones."

I dropped to my knees, laughing. "You're sitting here in a war-torn country in 105 degree heat, about to faint from lack of nourishment, and you only like orange ones?"

Carol started laughing so hard she couldn't answer. She gasped for breath and draped her body across the boxes for support. I leaned back into a pile of sorted baby clothes and rolled from side to side, holding my stomach, howling with laughter.

Our second mental balance tool is the "funnest": laughter. Statistics show that little kids laugh four hundred times a day. One study showed grownups laugh only eleven, and yet another said only four—and you know some people who can't meet even that quota!

According to the Association of Applied and Therapeutic Humor, an organization of doctors and healthcare professionals, science has proven that laughter kills tumor cells and fights diseases. They would like to see laughter become part of patients' written prescriptions. If a medicine had great physiological, psychological, and immunological effects, the FDA would be on it like crazy, regulating it and running trials on it. You wouldn't be able to get it for ten years. What's nice about human laughter is that it is free and has no side effects.

Stanford Medical School likened laughter to a form of physical exercise. It's like jogging on the inside. It lowers your blood pressure and heart rate, improves lung capacity, massages internal organs, increases memory and alertness, reduces pain, improves digestion, and lowers the stress hormones, cortisol and adrenaline. It's good for the muscles involved in laughter, your chest and abdomen, and it exercises those muscles not involved. Stanford said three to five minutes of laughter was as beneficial as three to five minutes of strenuous rowing. I don't know about you, but I'd much rather laugh than row.

After Norman Cousins cured himself with his laughter therapy, he did a study with two groups of people with pain. Half of them got a pain pill, and the other half got placebos. The half that got the placebos picked their own laughter therapy and did it for two hours every day. The results? The patients who had laughter therapy and the placebo had the same degree of pain control as those who took drugs.

In addition to physical benefits, laughter also offers psychological benefits. It teaches us to be out of control, brings us into the moment, helps us transcend our problems, brings us closer to people, and helps us think more clearly.

Research shows that even simply smiling has physical and

mental benefits. Smiling releases endorphins, natural pain killers, and serotonin. Together, these make us feel good. When you smile, immune function improves, and your blood pressure lowers. Smiling is a natural drug. My mama often advised, "When you see someone without a smile, give them one of yours." Wouldn't the world be a better, happier place if we all followed that old proverb?

Things that make us smile and laugh are all around us; we just need to be more receptive to finding them. These old favorites still do it for me!

Instructions on Dentyne gum...put one or two pieces in your mouth and chew.

Fritos...you could be a winner, no purchase necessary, details inside.

Microwave oven manual...do not use for drying pets.

Bread pudding...product will be hot after heating.

An iron...do not iron clothes on body.

Nytol sleeping aid...warning may cause drowsiness.

Dashboard windshield sun protector...do not drive with sun protector in place.

Harry Potter wizard broom...this broom does not actually fly.

Five hundred-piece jigsaw puzzle...some assembly required.

Blowtorch...do not use for drying hair.

On bottom of packaged dessert...do not turn upside down.

Children's cough medicine...do not drive a car or operate machinery after taking this medication. (I'm sure we could reduce the rate of construction accidents if we got those three-year-olds with colds off heavy equipment.)

Newspaper headlines are another great source of humor. These made me spew my breakfast cereal:

"Diaper Market Bottoms Out"
"Antique Stripper to Display Wares at Store"
"Lawyers Give Poor Legal Advice"
"Twenty-Year Friendship Ends at Altar"
"Queen Mary Having Bottom Scraped"

If we don't find enough to laugh about in our lives, then we must create opportunities for laughter.

Creating Laughter in Your Life

Make a list of things that make you laugh and add them to your everyday life.

Record, replay, and rent funny movies, shows, cartoons, and bloopers and watch them often.

Listen often to the comedian who makes you laugh until you wet your pants.

Plan a regularly scheduled comedy night.

Tough times at work and home? Each day, put a piece of tape on your sleeve indicating where you've had it up to.

Throw a party funded by money put into the laughter pot every time someone is caught being grumpy.

Write "FUN" on the top of every meeting's agenda and start with something funny.

Surround yourself with funny pictures of your friends and family and you.

Create a laughter bulletin board at work and home where everyone contributes cartoons, baby pictures, and so on.

Challenge others to have a best joke contest.

Buy funny greeting cards. Stop while you shop and read a few.

Listen to kids laugh. It's contagious.

As a child, did you ever gather your friends and play the game where you lay on the floor with your heads on each other's tummies? The first person starts to laugh, and before you know it, the laughter goes around the circle, and the whole bunch is in hysterics, giving a whole new meaning to "belly laugh."

Let's reclaim the laughter of our youth. It's a gift to ourselves, those around us, and our world.

Your Turn; Your Time for SelfCare

How many times a day do you laugh? Keep a record this month!

Just for fun, count how many times a day you "See someone without a smile and give them one of yours."

Get a blood pressure monitor or have someone take your blood pressure. Use your Creating Laughter list and laugh really hard for a few minutes! Take a second blood pressure reading two or three minutes after laughing. Is there a difference?

Recall a time when you laughed so hard you nearly lost your breath! Describe how you felt afterward. (Was your chest lighter, your tension released, your heart happier?)

Write a recollection of a time when someone was hurting and you witnessed or heard about laughter "healing" that person's mind, body, or spirit.

Can you recall a serious or solemn situation in which laughter was absolutely forbidden and you stifled your laugh so hard that you shook or grunted or spewed? Do share!

What four things will you do from the "Creating Laughter in Your Life" list? What other fun ideas do you have to add to that list?

Create a laughter bulletin board on your unit. Tell them LeAnn said so.

With your accountability partner: Share the funniest thing that happened to you this month. Did you laugh then? And all week when you thought about it?

Chapter 5

"I've Got to See This to Believe It"

Balancing your life mentally with positive thinking and visualization

Carol and I left the warehouse, where we had packed thousands of diapers, infant sleepers, and sets of baby clothes. Still chuckling from our jellybean moment, we went to find Cherie, who had been to the embassy to see when we were to leave. That's when we learned. We weren't.

Cherie explained that the Vietnamese government was annoyed with FCVN for having broken a regulation the day before. We were first on the list to leave on Operation Babylift, but now they not only took us off the number one position—they took us off the list.

When I heard that, I argued and insisted that we get our spot back. "That's not fair!" I protested. Sounds of gunfire in the night resounded in my head. "There must be something we can do!"

I continued arguing and begging, but my pleading was to no avail. Cherie said her hands were tied. Another organization would get the first plane.

"We still need to load just twenty babies onto the bus to take them to the Australian airliner, though," Cherie instructed. "We have a chapter and families waiting there too."

So, with heavy hearts, in scorching heat, we loaded babies

into the Volkswagen van. The middle seat had been removed, and I sat on the back bench seat. Ross handed me baby after baby, and I placed them on the seat next to me, then on mats laid on the floorboards. As they were packed in, kicking and waving their hands, one baby after another began to cry, creating a deafening symphony.

One hour later, traffic stopped in the airport drive. In front of us, near the end of the runway, an enormous black cloud billowed into the sky.

"Dear God! What's that, Ross?"

Before he could speculate, a man in a brown safari hat and khaki clothing approached our van. He identified himself as an Australian reporter and said, "The first plane load of orphans en route to the United States crashed just after takeoff."

Panic fluttered inside me. "No! That can't be true!"

"It's absolutely true," he insisted. "There was either a bomb on board that plane or it was shot down."

Dumbfounded, I grew angry. "This is exactly how rumors get started!" I snapped. "No one, not even in war, would deliberately bomb a plane full of babies!"

Someone hollered that the plane to Australia was ready to load, so we ended our debate. With a baby in each arm, I entered the aircraft and halted, immobilized by the sight. Hundreds of crying babies covered the floor of the plane. Canvases were stretched across parallel bars about six inches off the floor. Babies lay shoulder to shoulder on the long hammock-like rigs with a long seatbelt extending across their bodies, the entire length of the plane.

When our babies were loaded, I backed down the steps, the door slammed shut, and the plane slowly taxied away. Ross, Carol, and I started across the tarmac to the van, our eyes once again drawn to the enormous columns of smoke rising higher at the end of the runway.

As we drove away from the airport, I looked over my shoulder at the black plumes. The sound of the rescue helicopters battered overhead. I barely noticed the crowds and the noise as we drove back to the orphanage. *Could the Australian reporter be right?*

The office was awash with grief. Cherie threw her arms around Ross as we entered and through her tears told us what we'd refused to believe. The first flight of orphans leaving Saigon for America, the one I had begged to be on, crashed after takeoff, killing half of the four hundred babies and volunteers on board.

The plane had crashed. Then, so did I.

I slumped onto the rattan sofa, sobbing, shaking my head in my hands. I knew Mark listened to the news every morning while he shaved, and I could hear on the office radio what the news was reporting: FCVN first on the list for Operation Babylift. I couldn't call Mark and tell him I wasn't on the plane. There was no phone service out of Saigon.

"He'll think it's us!" I wailed. "I never should have come here—I never should have come here." I collapsed into Carol's arms and moaned through tears. "If they bomb one airlift plane, they'll bomb another. We might never get out of here alive."

Finally, I composed myself enough to go to Cherie, who was crying while sorting papers.

"Cherie," my voice quivered. "I'm sorry to have to say this, but I can't stay here and finish this airlift. I need to go home." I felt like a quitter and a coward.

She looked up and forced a reassuring smile. "This isn't America, LeAnn. You can't just go book a flight home. I'm afraid the only way you will get there is, eventually, on an airlift plane."

Numbly, I trudged to the nursery and robotically helped the

workers feed and diaper babies, trying to fake a positivity that evaded my breaking heart. *How can I find anything positive in this?*

As horrific as my situation was in Vietnam at that moment, I somehow tapped into my lifelong reservoir of positive thinking.

Positive Thinking

I'm a big believer in the power of positive thinking. I must have been born with positive genes. My mom was positive, and so was Dad in many ways. Even so, I've had to work hard to stay positive in this sometimes-negative world. I still read positive thinking books, listen to CDs, and practice what I preach. I'm sure you'll agree that it's hard to stay positive when the media, coworkers, community, and family members are negative. If I hadn't been a positive thinker, I probably wouldn't have gone to Vietnam, and I probably wouldn't have survived, even en route.

> *Viktor Frankl, a Jewish psychiatrist and author, survived the concentration camp of Auschwitz. He said, "Everything can be taken from a man but one thing, the last of human freedoms—to choose one's attitude in any given set of circumstances."*

When we were on our way and Carol's sister yelled and screamed, blamed and shamed us, it was hard for me to take all that negativity and stay positive. That's when I remembered the words my daddy had taught me: "Ninety percent of the things you worry about never happen, and the other 10 percent you can't change anyhow." I paraphrase it a little, saying, "And the other 10 percent I can handle."

It's said that the average person has forty thousand thoughts per day, of which 80 percent are negative. Every time you have a negative thought, your brain releases negative chemicals that make your body feel bad. Think about the last time you were upset. How did your body feel? Did your heart rate increase, your jaw clench, your breathing quicken? Now, imagine one of your happiest times. When you do so, your brain releases chemicals that make your body feel good. You'll notice a slower heartbeat, deeper, easier breathing, and relaxed muscles.

Kahlil Gibran wrote, "We choose our joys and sorrows long before we experience them."

Remember Norman Cousins, who checked himself out of the hospital and into a hotel for his self-prescribed laughter therapy and positive thinking? He was so convinced that these treatments affected his health and actually cured him that he left his twenty-five-year position as an editor to take a faculty position at UCLA Medical Center. With medical research, he demonstrated that panic, depression, hate, fear, and frustration can have negative effects on human health. There is mounting scientific evidence that hope, faith, love, the will to live, purpose, laughter, and festivity can actually help control disease. These aren't just mental states; they are physical conditions that create electromechanical connections that play a large part in the working of the immune system.

Norman Cousins had blood drawn prior to doing positive visualization. He imagined a magnificent world of peace and beauty. Five minutes later, his blood was drawn again, and he had a 200 percent increase in his T cells, a major immune system component.

When we combine positive visualization with positive thinking, even more remarkable changes occur.

Patients say they have less nausea and vomiting with chemotherapy when they visualize a serene white beach of Maui, cascading waterfalls, and peaceful sunsets. Apparently, that can also work in reverse. One cancer patient saw her doctor in the grocery store, and it brought back such intense images of nausea from her chemo that she threw up on the spot!

Dr. Norman Vincent Peale, a leader in positive thinking and visualization, had his patients who suffered from depression picture these letters on a neon sign: D.E.P.R.E.S.S.I.O.N. Then he had

George Washington University studied 119 healthy subjects who were instructed to imagine their white blood cells attacking cold and influenza cells. Researchers recorded a rise in their platelets and lymphocytes, cells that fight those illnesses.

them mentally extinguish the first two and the eighth letters. Instead of depression they visualized P.R.E.S.S O.N.

In a Canyon Ranch Health resort study on overweight people, exercisers were instructed to find a quiet spot, close their eyes, breathe deeply, and relax. Then they visualized each detail of their new selves—how slim they looked, how their new clothes fit, how their muscles were defined. They also imag- ined themselves eating small portions of healthy food. Participants who did this guided imagery lost twice as much weight as those who didn't.

Positive imagery is also effective in controlling anger. When we have a "short fuse," we can see it igniting. Then we must calmly visualize extinguishing it in our minds. Anger is one letter away from danger, and that's how it damages our health.

It took me too long to accept this truth: Our bodies and minds don't distinguish the difference between visualization and experience. They react as if both are real.

That's why visualization is widely used in sports. A basketball team was divided in half. One group shot free throws every day for an hour. The second group visualized shooting free throws an hour a day, sinking every one of them. At the competition they both performed equally.

The Texas Rangers baseball team was having a losing season back in the 70s, defeated nearly every game. The manager heard there was an evangelist in town, so he had the entire team wait in the dugout while he took all of the bats to be blessed by the evangelist. He came back later with blessed bats. The team went on to have a winning season and won the pennant! Were the bats blessed? It doesn't matter, does it? They believed they were, and that belief alone is what changed their bodies' actions.

Have you ever awoken from a nightmare, sweating, your heart racing?

Although the scary event didn't happen to you physically, your body responded as though it had. This phenomenon can work to our benefit, too. Recall your most successful moment and live it out again, visualizing it with all five senses. You can reclaim the same feelings again as your body releases the same chemicals as when you experienced it.

As you begin to incorporate more positive thinking and visualization into your days, consider that the very first fifteen minutes when you're barely awake in the morning is when our brains are most receptive. This alpha state, as it is called, is when we learn a lot and have some of our best ideas. Scientists are studying this most perceptive time for our brains and exploring whether, if we have predominantly negative thoughts during this time, it may set the tone of our whole day and maybe also our health and even our lives. What do you think about first thing in the morning? Are your thoughts positive? Or grumpy? Try using that first fifteen minutes to repeat positive affirmations. Create your own list, write them down, and read and repeat them often.

Positive Affirmations

I am relaxed and centered.

I love life.

I am living my priorities every day.

I am happy and blissful just being alive.

I am vibrantly healthy and radiantly beautiful.

I love doing my work, and I'm richly rewarded, creatively and financially.

The light of God within me is producing perfect results.

I always communicate truthfully, clearly, effectively, and lovingly.

I bring joy and laughter to all I do.

I invest my time wisely on what's really important.

My relationship with_____ is growing happier and more fulfilling every day.

I have enough time, energy, wisdom, and money to accomplish my desires.

At first, some of these affirmations are simply lies. "I don't feel the least bit centered," you say. But when you repeat something over and over to yourself, your brain begins to believe it and starts to respond to that and cues your body to do the same. It's important to use only positive words in affirmations because your brain doesn't hear the "no" word. For example, when I taught our son to play baseball, I reminded him to say, "I will hit the ball over the fence," not, "I won't strike out," because the brain only hears "strike out." One day I was carrying a cup of coffee, an armload of papers, and my car keys while trying to open the front door. (Why make two trips when you can make one difficult, time-consuming one?) In my head I was repeating, "Don't spill your coffee; don't spill your coffee." You guessed it. My brain did just what it heard, and I slopped my coffee down my white (of course) pants.

There are about three dozen secretions in the brain. It can write a thousand different prescriptions. One is endorphins. Another, interferon, affects the immune system and fights cancer and virus cells. A third example is neuropeptides. These chemicals translate emotions into bodily events. There are neuropeptide receptors in the brain and also in the lining of the colon, which is why we can have diarrhea with stress. Neuropeptide receptors are also in cells of the immune system, explaining how emotions affect our immune system.

Your brain can literally be "rewired" with positive thinking. Some neurological connections are strengthened while others are replaced. New thoughts and images stimulate new pathways in the brain and, when constantly repeated, have a great impact on behavior. For example, if you constantly think, "I'm so annoyed with my husband" and think of all the irritating things he does, you are strengthening those neurological connections. Those thoughts and images become a part of your strong belief system, and that affects your mood, behavior, and relationship. If being annoyed with your husband is your objective, you will achieve it with this mental training. If growing your loving relationship is your goal, you need to change your mental engineering, using positive thoughts and images. Make lists of all you love about him—long lists—and review and repeat them often. Soon you brain will be rewired, and your thoughts, images, and actions will change. The more you repeat, "I love my man!" the greater the neurological impact.

If you find yourself mentally repeating negative thoughts about a person or situation, write them down as they occur throughout the day. Writing them releases negative emotions and makes way for a new script. After three or four days, target the most frequent or disruptive thoughts to rewrite. For example, one working mom found herself writing, "I'm the first one up in the morning and the last one to sleep at night, and nobody appreciates all I do." Then she rewrote it as, "I love my family, and I choose to show that love in all I do for them." Soon, her attitude changed, as did her actions, and, consequently, her family's.

As you're implementing positive visualization to actualize your goals, remember to appreciate what you have along the way. One woman visualizing a Corvette convertible complained negatively every day about her rusty old van. Be grateful that you have a car as you visualize a better one.

Positive thinking and imaging are powerful and mysterious forces in human nature, capable of bringing about dramatic improvement in our lives. Einstein said, "Imagination is more powerful than knowledge." It's a kind of mental engineering. Your mind is a computer; you have sovereign control over the input.

How are you going to incorporate positive thinking and visualization to change your life?

Your Turn; Your Time for SelfCare

Think about the last time you were upset. How did your body feel? Did your heart rate increase, your jaw clench, your breathing quicken?

Now, imagine one of your happiest times. Close your eyes and meditate on that image and feeling for a few minutes. How does your body feel?

Who were/are the most positive people in your life? List them here. Do you surround yourself with them?

When was the last time you were with them? What did you do with them?

Who are the stinkin' thinkers, the negative people in your life? List them here. (Unless you're married to them, spend less time with them. ☺)

Review the list of "Positive Affirmations." Create your own list. Post it where you can read it; then, repeat it ten times a day, every day.

What specific image are you going to visualize and what positive affirmations are you going to repeat during the first fifteen minutes of your day?

Can you recall an occasion or story you've heard in which positive thinking and visualization changed an outcome in health, sports, relationship, or a career? Describe it.

Create a vision board from a large piece of paper, tag board, or cardboard. On it paste pictures of things you want to achieve: personal goals, professional goals, material goods, spiritual needs, physical accomplishments, family desires, and so on. Add inspirational words, quotations, and affirmations you want to live by. Put it in a place where you see it every day. Your subconscious mind will direct your actions. Watch this positive visualization become a reality.

With your accountability partner: Compare how you feel with positive people as opposed to how you feel with negative ones. Also, share and describe your vision board.

Chapter 6

"How Can I Possibly Forgive This?"

Balancing your life mentally with forgiveness

We all busied ourselves in the office, completing paperwork for Operation Babylift.

"LeAnn, it's for you," Sister said.

I almost laughed. It seemed like a joke. "Who'd call me in Saigon?"

An Associated Press reporter was on the line saying an Iowa City reporter had, incredibly, contacted him to learn whether I had been on the fatal crash. The reporter could now call Mark and tell him I was safe. The man asked if I had any other messages for my husband.

Any messages. There was so much I wanted to say. So much he needed to know.

"Just tell him I'm okay and I love him very much," I choked.

I hung up the phone. "Oh, thank God!" Slumping onto the couch next to Carol, I sighed with relief. "My family will know I'm alive and well. Their not knowing was killing me inside." The heavy blanket of regret and fear began to lift.

Reinvigorated, I looked around at the babbling babies, took a deep breath, and almost shouted, "Let's get to work!"

The tragedy only intensified the fever pitch of the airlift plans and certainly hadn't slowed the arrival of more children. Our census had doubled to two hundred. Yet, because so many foster mothers stayed and several Vietnamese nurses came to help, the infant care was outstanding. Just very crowded and very loud.

With renewed enthusiasm and hope I picked up a fussing baby from a mat on the office floor. My head and heart began to release the ruinous grief, worry, guilt, and helplessness. The walls and floors seemed to vibrate with the sounds of crying and chattering.

"We'll be working into the night," Cherie said as she plopped a stack of files onto the table. "Remember I told you how the Vietnamese government wouldn't allow Amerasian babies to have registered legal names or birth certificates?"

I wiped a baby's bottom and tucked the diaper beneath it. "I remember."

"Well, they just made a new rule. Every baby leaving on Operation Babylift has to have a legal name and birth certificate."

"What?" Ross asked incredulously.

"How are we going to manage that?" I wondered out loud.

Cherie nodded to the adjoining room, where a man in a white lab coat worked intently over a child. "Dr. Cuong is here, as he is almost every night. He'll do physicals on all the babies and estimate how old they are. We, then, will assign them birth dates and make up proof-of-birth-statements, which the government says they'll accept."

She pulled hospital ID bracelets from one of the eighteen boxes we'd delivered and tossed them to Ross. Then she handed Sister Terese a Vietnamese name book and quipped, "By morning every baby will have a certificate and a legal name."

Dr. Cuong joined us and began to examine another baby

tenderly. As he provided information, we provided a name, and Sister Terese typed it on the ID bracelet.

"Hey, this is Jeni," Ross said of a cutie in his arms. "That's all we've ever called her."

"Jeni ain't gonna cut it getting her out of the country," Sister teased as she looked in her book of names.

"Is this legal?" Carol couldn't help but ask.

"We didn't make up the rules; they did," Cherie said. "We just have to find a way to comply."

I cuddled the baby in my arms, trying to purge from my mind images of the fiery crash. *How many babies died? How many volunteers...like me?* And now it seemed the Vietnamese government was making it as hard as possible for us to save these babies. I despised the war. I hated the bombing. How could they do this to babies? *How can I ever forgive this?*

Forgiveness

This fourth and final mental balance tool may be the hardest, yet possibly the most important. We waste a lot of our energy, our health, and even our lives when we fail to forgive.

So, starting today, we forgive, first of all, ourselves. For any past mistakes, indiscretions, or regretted decisions, we forgive ourselves. What we did back then was who we were then, based on what we knew then. It has nothing to do with who we choose to be today.

And starting today, we forgive somebody else, no matter how horrific the offense. Remember, when we refuse to forgive someone, it doesn't hurt them; it only hurts us. Why would we give someone who wounded us so deeply the power to continue to harm us with sleepless nights, upset stomachs, and headaches.

We must forgive. It is freeing and healing.

Organized religion and twelve-step programs have long recognized the healing power of forgiveness. New research shows that it has helped people break through intergenerational cycles of revenge, anger, and bitterness to resolve resentment within relationships.

Science has shown that people who won't forgive have more illnesses, lower immune system function, and increased heart disease. They also have higher divorce rates, less social support, and more depression.

Positive visualization is an effective forgiveness tool. Visualizing a quarrel ended, a relationship restored, the pain and alienation eliminated is a tremendous first step. Sometimes you can confront the offender directly, but often that is not possible or advisable. Then, it may help to imagine vividly the face of the person who has wronged you and to say out loud, "I forgive you." Writing a letter, whether you send it or not, releasing the other person—and you—can promote the healing. A widely accepted definition of forgiveness is to pardon, to release from further punishment.

Equally important is to accept forgiveness. It's an antidote for poisons that can corrupt the body and damage the soul.

The University of Northern Iowa studied women who were counseled with the forgiveness option. After one year the experimental group had less depression and more self-esteem.

Forgiveness sometimes feels like a short-term loss for a real long-term gain. Some consider it a weakness, but it demands great spiritual strength and moral courage, both in granting and accepting it. So, write the letter, make the call, or say it face to face—whatever it takes, just let it go—move on.

Steps to Forgiveness

1) Realize you have been unjustly treated and have a right to be angry.

2) Decide that forgiveness is an option of choice, a positive decision. It doesn't always equal forgetting, and sometimes there is no reconciliation.

3) Make a commitment to yourself to do what it takes to forgive, knowing you deserve to be healed and released from the suffering.

4) Put your grievance story into words, if only for yourself, stating exactly what happened and how you feel about it. (At the moment you feel upset, practice your stress-management techniques to soothe your body's flight or fight response.)

5) Recognize that your primary distress now is coming from the hurt feelings and thoughts and the physical upset you are suffering now, not what offended you or hurt in the past.

6) Reframe the offender. Acknowledging how they were raised and treated themselves helps reveal how they were probably victims of similar treatment while not condoning or excusing it.

7) Allow yourself to begin to develop feelings of empathy or even compassion for the offender, not because of what the person did, but in spite of it.

8) Give up expecting things from other people that they do not choose to give you. Remind yourself that you can create you own health, love, peace, and prosperity and work hard to get them.

9) Finally, you can forgive, remembering that a life well lived is the best "revenge." Instead of focusing on your wounded feelings and thereby giving your offender power over you, claim your personal power.

10) Add a new ending to your grievance story, including the heroic choice you made to forgive.

Mark Twain wrote, "Forgiveness is the fragrance a violet sheds on the heel that crushes it."

Forgiveness is an empowering choice. Sometimes forgiving other people is the greatest gift we can give ourselves.

Your Turn; Your Time for SelfCare

What one past mistake, decision, or indiscretion will you forgive yourself for, starting today?

Consider writing it on a piece of paper, placing it in a fireproof container, and safely burning it. Let your regret, guilt, and remorse rise and evaporate with the smoke. Then pause awhile, soaking up a renewed feeling of relief and love. How does that feel?

What person do you need to forgive? Consider writing a letter releasing that person (and you). Mailing it is optional. Immerse yourself in the feeling of release.

If you believe in a Higher Power, rest in prayerful meditation, asking God for forgiveness, knowing there is nothing you can say or do that is unforgivable.

If needed, what books will you read or counselor will you seek to get more help to forgive?

With your accountability partner: Describe the process of identifying and forgiving the person you selected this month. How has this process been helpful to you?

Chapter 7

"So, Help Me, God"

Balancing your life spiritually

At 3:00 A.M. Carol stretched out on the rattan couch, and I curled up on the floor of the office. A few hours later I awoke to sunshine in my eyes and squinted, expecting to see the Madonna and Child picture on my bedroom wall at home. Instead, a gecko stared at me, reminding me where I was.

Carol and I sauntered to the kitchen for my usual cola and French bread breakfast.

Cherie and Ross greeted me with particularly bright smiles. This is when Cherie often gave us our assignments for the day, but I was totally unprepared for this one.

She broke a piece of soft bread from the loaf. "LeAnn, you and Mark will be adopting one of those babies in the next room."

I sat stunned. In all the commotion I hadn't considered that our two-year wait for a child would be dramatically shortened now. Before I could comprehend her point, she went on. "You can wait to be assigned a son from across a desk in Denver...." She paused to touch my hand. "Or you can go in there and choose a son."

Speechless and dazed, my heart raced with excitement, then

fear. "Really?" I finally croaked. Surely, I had heard her wrong.

Cherie's tired eyes danced. "Really."

"So, I can just go in there and pick out a son?" I almost felt dizzy at the thought.

Cherie nodded again. Carol and Ross snickered at my inability to comprehend the message.

I turned to Carol. "Come with me." She jumped up immediately, and we approached the door to the nursery together.

I paused and took a deep breath. "This is like a fantasy. A dream come true."

One of the last things I had told Angela and Christie was that our baby wasn't ready yet and wouldn't be coming home with me. Now, in this world of incredible events, something even more incredible was about to happen.

Expectantly, I pushed open the door. Babies on blankets and mats, in boxes and baskets and bassinets and cribs.

"Carol, how will I ever choose? There are nearly two hundred babies here now."

"Some are girls," she offered. "That'll limit your choices a little."

I almost laughed. "I've heard of exciting shopping sprees before, but this is ridiculous! I wish Mark were here."

One baby in a white T-shirt and diaper looked at me with bright eyes. I picked him up and sat cross-legged on the floor with him on my lap. He seemed to be about nine months old and responded to my words with cute facial expressions and animation. I noticed he had a second bracelet on his ankle, with a family name on it. He was already assigned.

Another child caught my eye as he pulled himself to his feet beside a wooden crib. We watched with amusement as he tugged at the toes of the baby sleeping inside. His eyes met mine, then he dropped to his hands and knees and began crawling to me. I met him halfway across the room and picked him up. He wore only a diaper, and his soft round tummy bulged over its rim. He smiled brightly at me, revealing chubby cheeks and deep dimples. As I hugged him, he nestled his head into my shoulder.

"Maybe you'll be our son," I whispered. He pulled back, staring into my eyes, still smiling. I carried him around the room, looking at every infant, touching one, talking to another. The baby in my arms babbled, smiled, and continued to cuddle. I couldn't bring myself to put him down as we went upstairs, where the floor was carpeted with even more babies. The hallway was like a megaphone.

"Let me hold him," Carol coaxed, "while you look at the others."

I wove my way to the blanket at the end of the room and sat caressing the infants there. As I cradled one in my arms, I could feel the bones of his spine press against my skin. Another's eyes looked glazed and motionless. Sorrow gripped me.

The little boy Carol was carrying for me patted my shoulder. As I turned to look, he reached his chubby arms out to me. Taking him from her, I snuggled him close.

Someone had loved him very much.

Downstairs, we meandered from mat to crib, looking at all the infants again. I wished I could adopt them all. But I knew there were long waiting lists at the Denver headquarters of hundreds of families who had completed the tedious, time-consuming application process. Each of these precious orphans would have immediate homes, carefully selected for them.

"How do I choose?" I asked myself as much as Carol. Recalling our chosen name, I muttered, "Which one is our Mitch?"

The baby boy in my arms answered by patting my face.

I sat on the floor, slowly rocking him back and forth in my arms. I whispered a prayer for the decision I was about to make. "Help me, God," I prayed. "Show me, Lord, that this decision is right."

The baby snuggled into the hollow of my neck. I could feel his shallow breath and tender skin as he embraced my neck and my heart.

I recalled all the data we had collected, all the letters of references from friends, bankers and employers, all the interviews with the social workers.

It had all been worth it for this moment.

We rocked in silence, clinging to each other. Then, with tears in my eyes and immense joy in my heart, I walked back through the nursery door to the office. "Meet our son, Mitchell Thieman!" I announced, hardly believing my own words. Ross, Sister, and Cherie gathered around and hugged us. Cherie brought a name tag, and I eagerly scrawled "Reserve for Mark Thieman" on it and placed it on Mitchell's ankle. Joyful tears streamed down my cheeks. For a moment all my fears were gone. I no longer wondered why I had been driven to make this journey. "This is why God sent me to Vietnam," I whispered.

I had been sent to choose our son.

Are there days you wonder, *Are you there, God?* Are there times you feel the Divine presence and guidance in your life, and other times when you wonder how they got so far away? On those days, remember, it wasn't God who moved.

Creating a spiritual balance in our lives is as crucial as the mental and physical, for we cannot cope in our war zones without it.

Polls estimate that over 92 percent of Americans believe in God. If you are among that majority, I call on you to be in touch with the God you believe in every single day. We can't just wait for weekends.

Even if it is just for fifteen minutes, take time for prayer, meditation, or reflection. Yet I know in our frenetic lives that we barely have time to eat, sleep, and exercise, so it is a real challenge to create another fifteen minutes to nurture ourselves spiritually. Yet it is critical to our survival.

As I was grappling with this lack of discipline in my life, I happened to talk to a friend who was telling me, in idle conversation, about his busy week. He had worked over sixty hours, driven sixty miles to Denver several times, harvested his garden, and even visited a friend's brother in jail. Then he casually mentioned something that came to him during his hour of prayer that morning.

I interrupted. "Bob, I can barely find time for fifteen minutes; how do you do an hour?"

Then he said the words that still echo in my head every day. "If I didn't start my day that way, I would never have time for the rest."

That's when I bought my little daily reading book. After trying to read it while drying my hair every morning, I finally realized I was supposed to sit down... shut up... and listen.

A twenty-eight year study of 5,200 men and women, including Jews, Muslims, Buddhists, and a broad variety of Christian denominations, plus atheists and agnostics, found frequent service attendees had healthier lifestyles. They were more likely to quit smoking, increase exercising, reduce weight, be less depressed, and stay married.

Listen. To that deep inner voice. You can call it intuition, the Holy Spirit, gut feeling—whatever fits your spiritual beliefs. Few of us see burning bushes or hear the actual voice of God, but we all have the inner voice, which is the Divine guidance for our lives, and we cannot hear it in the chaos.

I soon learned that fifteen minutes was a great investment. Within a few weeks I noticed I was happier, more centered, more productive—a better person.

One night on the evening news I saw Dan Rather interviewing Mother Teresa. He asked, "What do you say when you pray?" She said, "Nothing. I just listen." Dan queried, "What does God say?" She answered, "Nothing. He just listens."

In that listening-silence is the wisdom, the guidance, the direction we can only "hear" in peace and quiet.

Modern medicine is finally learning that we are not just physical beings, but spiritual beings too, and the spirit has a great effect on healing. The American Medical Association requires medical schools to teach students to inquire about a patient's religion. Eighty percent of medical schools address spirituality in their curricula because of the impact on patients' health. Ninety-nine percent of doctors believe there is an important relationship between the spirit and the flesh.

The University of Colorado proved that twenty-year-olds who go to church once a week will live on average to eighty-two, whereas their peers who never attend religious service will die on average at age seventy-five. Even when people with similar incomes, lifestyles,

Duke University discovered that people who attend church, temple, or mosque regularly have half the levels of the blood protein interleukin-6, which, in high levels, is associated with AIDS, cancer, osteoporosis, diabetes, and Alzheimer's. Patients affiliated with a religious community had 50 percent shorter hospital stays than those with no religious affiliation.

and behaviors were compared, a longevity gap remained. The researchers conclude that church goers have meaning in their lives, a better sense of control, and can relate better to other people. These all have positive health benefits.

Harvard's Mind/Body Institute agrees that prayer and religious ritual can relieve stress. Praying ten to twenty minutes a day can decrease blood pressure, heart rate, breathing, and metabolic rates.

In one study, half of nearly four hundred subjects received prayer while the other half did not. Neither group was told about the prayers. Those who were prayed for had half as many complications and needed less medication than those who were not prayed for.

Believing and trusting in a Higher Power takes most of the stress off in life. When you know it is not all up to you, that God has a plan and you trust that, all you have to do is your very best and then let go. Let go and let God.

I only know one scripture reading by heart. Every morning, without exception, I say these words from the 25th Psalm: "Show me Your way, oh Lord. Teach me Your path. Lead me in Your truth and teach me." I change the next line by adding my own: "because I don't know what the heck I'm doing." But God does. Trusting that takes away the worry.

Surely you, too, can find ten to twenty minutes a day for spiritual balance, so it becomes a habit, a daily coping tool. This practice helps build a spiritual reserve. Without it, you may be barely keeping a balance on the spiritual tightrope; then, when something shakes the rope, you may lose your grip.

Consider joining the 90 percent of Americans who pray. Boost the 40 percent who go to church weekly.

So often we choose a way of life that best suits our bodies... let's decide on one that also nurtures our souls.

10 Ways to Pray, Meditate, Reflect...and Listen

1) Set aside time, even just fifteen minutes, to be alone and quiet. Relax your mind and body. Breathe. Hush your heart. Bid all your senses be still. Listen. In the silence, you will get a sense, a feeling, an intuition that will guide you. Respect and follow that.

2) Talk to God in a simple manner, yammering on about what is on your mind. Formal language and prayer—even words— are not necessary. God will understand you.

3) Utilize your positive thinking and affirmations. Repeat, "I believe I am always Divinely guided. I believe I will make the right choices. I believe God will make the way."

4) Utilize your positive visualization. Imagine a blackboard with jumbled words, phrases, and wrong answers—in short, a sorry record of mistakes. Then, imagine the Creator sweeping a sponge across it, wiping it clean. Release the guilt. God forgave you. Forgive yourself. It's a simple as that.

5) Repeat, "With God's help, I now forgive." Anger, resentment, and hatred set up barriers that deprive us of spiritual power. Let go and let God do the judging and punishing of others.

6) Surrender a problem. Trust a Higher Power at work, healing you and solving your difficulties.

7) Utilize prayer minutes. Talk to God throughout the day, on the subway, at your desk, while folding laundry. Close your eyes and have a word or two with God. Feel your Creator's presence. Can't close your eyes? (Not a good idea on the Interstate.) Use that time to talk to God anyway.

8) Make family prayer time—perhaps a short prayer with a meal or before bed. Light a candle. Set aside a sacred time.

9) Practice thanksgiving. Be less concerned about what you lack and more grateful for all you have.

10) Join a faith community. Study holy works. Read inspirational writings. Surround yourself with faith-filled people and places.

Your Turn; Your Time for SelfCare

Are you currently spending quiet time in daily meditation, reflection, and/or prayer?

If not, in what part of your day will you schedule fifteen minutes for this spiritual time?

What books will you read daily for reflection and/or prayer?

Review the "10 Ways to Pray, Meditate, Reflect…and Listen" list. What one thing will you implement this week? And what one thing next week? And the next?

Get a blood pressure monitor or have someone take your blood pressure. Take your blood pressure before your meditation/prayer time. Then take it again afterward. Do you notice a difference?

List ten things you are thankful for:

Write letters of gratitude to five people who have helped you in life. List them here. For what are you grateful?

With your accountability partner: What meditative and or prayerful community would you like to explore being a part of?

What specific steps will you take to do so?

Chapter 8

"I Want My 'Juice!'"

Asking for what you need to put your life in better balance

"We're outta here!" Ross nearly leapt into the room. "We leave this afternoon!" He motioned to the babies on the floors, in infant seats, clothes baskets, cribs, and boxes. "Pack up!" he ordered with a laugh.

Workers in every room began dressing the babies for their homecomings. Infants were changed from their daily attire of diapers and sleepers into their Sunday best. I beamed like a proud mama to see them in shorts, shirts, and ruffle dresses we had shipped from Iowa. Now the clothes were going back to the States—on a baby—going home.

The women, who had previously diapered and fed them so merrily, now openly cried as they dressed them one last time. Many of the foster mothers who had come to help wept as they prepared to relinquish the babies they had cared for as their own. We hugged them, barely able to imagine their feelings. "We're so happy for them," one said in tearful, broken English.

In the kitchen, workers prepared hundreds of glass bottles of formula. When I noticed each was boiling hot, I cautioned the woman at the stove. In choppy English she reported that it had been done deliberately, under the assumption that the formula would cool and be just the right temperature by the time we boarded the plane. She smiled proudly at what she thought was an ingenious idea.

I hoped she was right.

The city bus that was to transport the babies to the airport was too large to maneuver the narrow streets near the center, so it parked a mile or so away on the main street. We loaded the babies into the Volkswagen van to take them to the bus. The center seat was removed, and I sat on the back bench seat. We placed twenty-two babies all around me on the seat and floor, as we had done for the trip to the Australian flight.

That was before the crash.

My heart jolted with fear, and I gripped the baby in my arms. *Would our flight be bombed or sabotaged too?* My worry was interrupted by the sounds of more babies crying and the pressures of the task at hand.

Ross slowly snaked the van to the waiting city bus. The infants were too crowded to roll around as it crept through the narrow street. We carried the wee ones onto the big bus and placed them three on a seat—or four if they were little. Then the van returned to the center for more.

After four trips, the city bus was full to capacity. Once we got this first bus of one hundred babies delivered to the airport, we'd return for the second hundred...and Mitch. I had hugged him and kissed his chin and cheeks, explaining that he'd be on the next load and we would leave for home together. Home. I grinned, imagining him there with his daddy and sisters.

Now every baby on every seat of the city bus was bawling. We had placed their heads against the seat backs to prevent them from rolling forward when the bus slowed or stopped. The task of transporting them safely seemed monumental.

Carol, Ross, and I placed ourselves in the aisles to watch over them as the bus slowly inched its way to the airport. The motion of the bus and the hum of the motor soothed some of the infants, but the three of us still had to shout to be heard above the wailing. We stretched our arms and legs to guard the babies from falling, and we laughed as we looked at one another balancing spread eagle, trying to steady the precious cargo.

"I think I saw this on *I Love Lucy* once!" I shouted. Carol and Ross laughed in spite of the stress. I knew, certainly, that there was no time to make better accommodations for transportation. Vietnam's President Thieu had set a time and date for their departure, and it was FCVN's problem to meet that deadline. His seemingly deliberate efforts to make the airlift fail only served to strengthen our conviction to make it succeed.

There were a few older children on board, and they tended to the babies placed beside them. A little girl with straight black hair patted the backs of the three babies next to her as she cooed to them in Vietnamese. I listened as another boy sang native songs while rocking the baby whimpering in his arms. The bus driver turned the corners at a snail's pace and we moved from seat to seat, patting, soothing, and stabilizing squalling babies.

They each looked so cute in their frills and fancy clothes, but their little arms and legs flailed as they screamed simultaneously. Four toddlers, probably only two or three years old, sat together on the last seat of the bus. As their sweaty little bodies jostled in the sweltering heat, they gazed at all the bawling babies, and one by one they joined in the chorus of tears.

"Juice!" one pleaded. "Juice!"

When a toddler figures out what he needs, he asks for it until he gets it. "I want juice. I want juice. I want juice. I want juice. I want juice!"—until someone gets the kid some juice!

Take time—quiet time—to evaluate your life. Is your physical, mental, or spiritual self a little out of balance? What is lacking? What do you need more of? How can others support you in acquiring it? Give this careful thought, then make a list. Then be more like babies and toddlers and ask for what you need to get your life in better balance again. Ask for your "juice" lovingly—from yourself, your family, your supervisor, your coworkers—to get the time and support you need to nurture your body, mind, and spirit.

Science is proving more and more the critical connection between body, mind, and spirit. It has been irrevocably proven that anxiety, alienation, and hopelessness are not just mental states. Neither are love, serenity, and optimism. All are physiological states that affect our health, just as clearly as obesity or physical fitness. The challenge is to nurture each system to sustain and heal the others.

On the one hand, it might seem a little discouraging to think that physical pain and disease cannot be confined to our bodies but spread to our emotional and mental well-being. On the other hand, it's encouraging to know that because the physical, mental, and spiritual aspects are interrelated, we can call upon all three to find healing in times of brokenness.

As we try to balance our lives physically, mentally, and spiritually, it often helps to combine the three aspects. Some people enjoy prayer-walking to care for their bodies and spirits at the same time. You can listen to a spiritual CD as you walk, sing a hymn, or simply yammer on and on to God (who is always listening).

A Harvard study bears out the fact that relaxation with yoga, prayer, or simple deep-breathing exercises can help counter the effects of chronic stress and improve our health.

Many people listen to motivational tapes while exercising, combining the physical and mental. Some listen to comedians to work their minds and bodies with laughter. Others listen to religious music or spiritual CDs when they work out.

On the too-rare occasions that I clean my house, I like to do it to old-time rock 'n' roll. I reminisce about the days of old while I vacuum my house in record time, getting great exercise. Endorphins are released while I jitterbug and dust, clearing my mind and my house at the same time.

I sing entire show tunes while I drive my car. Singing is great for my lungs and a great endorphin releaser for my mind. When I get to a stop sign, singing the soundtrack from Camelot at the top of lungs, I look around and notice everybody around me is laughing. So, I figure it is a good endorphin releaser for others too. We all win.

You too can combine the physical, mental, and spiritual in simple creative ways. Take a walk or hike to a peaceful setting, then relax there. Walk or bike to your next appointment, enjoying the sites, nurturing your five senses, clearing your mind. Sleep in late on a Saturday morning, then awaken and read an inspirational book. Massages, manicures, and herbal baths are lovely ways to nourish the mind, body, and spirit too.

Take quiet time to examine your life, then politely, with no whining, say, "I want my juice."

Your Turn; Your Time for SelfCare

Where on this line would you chart your life balance, physically, mentally, and spiritually?

0--/--10
No balance   Very balanced

What one thing will you do to put your life better in balance physically?

What one thing will you do to put your life better in balance mentally?

What one thing will you do to put your life better in balance spiritually?

With your accountability partner: What specific activities will you create to nurture your mind, body, and spirit simultaneously?

Put them on your schedule.

Chapter 9

"What Do We Do Now?"

Living your priorities

It seemed like hours passed before we arrived at the gates of the airport. Another gun-bearing, mean-looking Vietnamese guard stopped the bus, and our driver motioned for Ross to come forward. Ross began to argue with the guard in Vietnamese. He turned to us and shouted, "President Thieu has canceled our flight. We have to wait for clearance."

Carol and I groaned in unison.

Ross turned back to the guard. "We can't just wait in this bus with all these babies. It's one hundred and eight degrees outside and even hotter in here!" The babies cried even louder since the bus was not in motion.

"These babies are going to lose a lot of fluid in these tears," I shouted over the din. "And the heat will cause diarrhea, which will make them dehydrate for sure." I scrambled to find the formula. "It's still boiling hot! Now what'll we do?"

Parked in the sun, the van became an oven. We began picking up one baby, then another, in a frenetic effort to comfort as many as possible while Ross continued to appeal to the guard. Perspiration plastered our clothes to us, and sweat dripped from our faces.

As the air inside the bus grew hotter, the little ones grew more frantic. Stroking their damp hair, I blew gently into their faces and waved a diaper as a fan. How sorrowfully ironic that we had cases of formula but nothing to feed the squalling cargo.

Slowly, the bus inched forward through the opening gates.

"They're letting us use the Quonset huts while we wait for this mess to get straightened out," Ross yelled, sounding relieved.

"Maybe we should go back to the center in the meantime so we can take better care of these babies," Carol called back. "They won't be able to take much more of this."

"No way!" Ross bellowed. "That's just what they want us to do. We are not leaving until the babies are on that plane!"

We carried the infants inside the metal Quonset huts. Their pretty clothes clung to their wet little bodies as they continued to cry. I watched as a little passenger, about five years old, struggled to carry the baby he'd been tending. As the tiny body slid down in his arms, his face grimaced, and his muscles tightened as he clutched the baby closer.

The words to the theme song from the slide show I had presented so many times came to my mind: "He ain't heavy, he's my brother." I blinked back tears. How sad that he had to carry one so small. How wonderful that he would.

The old building was filthy inside. Cobwebs and dust hung from the metal walls. We carefully placed the little ones on cut-up cardboard boxes and blankets on the dirty concrete floor. The small windows near the ceiling were so grimy that light could barely shine through.

The sounds of the crying echoed off the sides of the tin walls. The muggy air inside the Quonset hut threatened to smother our efforts. Carol ran the bottles of formula under water at the drinking fountain and then handed them to me one at a time. I fed the babies as fast as I could.

Finally, Ross returned with the latest word from airport officials. "President Thieu will let only this one plane load of orphans leave."

Quickly, I began to gather babies and headed for the bus. Ross stopped me. "You didn't hear me, LeAnn. I said one plane. To be sure you see Mark and your girls again, you have got to get on this one."

"What about the rest of the babies?" I refused to hear his message. "What about Mitch?"

Ross put his hands on my shoulders and stared into my eyes. "I'm staying, LeAnn, and I promise I'll try to get him and bring him to you in the States. But now you have got...to...go...home."

I stepped into his arms, buried my head in his chest, and bawled like the babies.

My frantic mind tried to think of what to do. Then I remembered my priorities. My family. And I knew.

"I'm not leaving without my son!"

"Do you know what you're saying?"

I threw my arms in the air. "I can't go home without him!"

"Go, then," Ross said. "I'll try to hold the plane until you get back."

I knew he would be powerless to do so, but he explained the plan to the bus driver as I climbed its stairs two at a time.

The same bus that crept so slowly en route to the airport now sped rapidly, almost recklessly back toward the center with me as its only passenger. The crowded streets, the hundreds of weaving bicycles, and the lane-less convoy of cars angered me as the bus honked and jerked through the snarled traffic.

Why couldn't they hurry?

Why couldn't they clear a path?

Didn't they know this was literally a matter of life and death?

Already I couldn't imagine my life without Mitchell.

Finally, the driver stopped on the main street, opened the door, smiled, and pointed down the narrow road ahead. I jumped off the bus and raced down the dirt street toward the center.

Breathless, I ran and prayed out loud, "Please, God, please let me get there in time to get Mitch and get back."

The strap of my sandal broke. My shoe flopped wildly against my ankle. I grabbed it without breaking stride, clenched it in my fist, and ran in barefoot, with all my might.

"Please, Lord," I wheezed. "My family is my priority. Now Mitch is family. Please let them hold the plane!"

My side ached fiercely as I pushed harder. The center was in sight. Numbness and burning fired through my legs. Panting and puffing, I ran through the courtyard gates, up the steps, and into the office. Cherie looked up, startled.

"I've got to get Mitch! I've got to get back!"

Cherie interrupted. "I know, I know," she said, easing me into a chair. "I just got off the phone with the government and the airport. They're holding the plane."

I beamed a smile while gasping for breath.

She waited for me to catch my wind before she continued. Officials had notified her that the flight would wait for additional babies, and a second flight had been approved to leave too.

Still panting, I hurried into the next room, and across the nursery I saw Mitch, waiting in a white shirt and red-checkered playsuit. I'd only been his mother for three days, but he raised his arms to me as if to say, "I never doubted you for a minute, Mom."

Truly living our priorities can be a real challenge. Periodically, we need to evaluate the priorities in our lives.

What is your number-one priority? Are you living it?

I know it may sound a bit challenging when I suggest that priorities are not what we state them to be but how we're spending our time. Obviously, what we're spending our time doing is what we have established as our priorities, is it not?

Failing to truly live the priorities in our lives causes stress, resentment, and feelings of inadequacy, in spite of our best efforts. Examining and deciding how we spend our time is the key to resolving this conflict. (We'll explore this concept more in the next chapter.)

Although teens typically rebuff parental overtures, they want parents to keep trying. The Institute for Youth Development in Washington, D.C., studied 429 kids from ages eleven to fourteen and found they wanted more connectedness with their parents and more time doing simple things together. While 28 percent of dual-earner parents said they play or exercise with their children every day, only a miniscule 6 percent of kids agreed that was the case.

When asked to identify their top priority, many people quickly reply, "My family." Yet, were you as shocked as I to learn that the average parent and child in this country spend twelve minutes a day one-on-one, six of which are negative?

A simple (not easy, but simple) gesture for living priorities is to resurrect the family supper. I was a stickler about this when the kids were home, and I must admit the importance of it was not as clear to them at the time as it was to me. It was often a pain in the tush to rearrange dinner around ballet, baseball, Boy Scouts, and horse poop. But we had supper together, even if it was at 7:30. They didn't grumble about it often because the expectation had

The City of Cincinnati conducted a study showing that teenagers who ate supper with their families did better in school, had better friendships, and had fewer problems with depression and drugs.

> *It costs four times as much to send a kid to the state pen as it does to send him or her to Penn State.*

been established long before, and they knew it was non-negotiable.

Family meals say to our children, "Being with you is important to me. Nothing else matters more." Obeying the rule of only positive talk at the table allows for wonderful conversations and connectedness.

Until we make the proper raising of our children the number-one priority of our nation, we will continue to have social woes. People without children have an important, irreplaceable role in the raising or our children too. Aunts, uncles, big brothers, and big sisters can often impact a child's life in a way that parents cannot.

There is an African tribal greeting used between neighboring tribes, "Abantwani Joni." It means, "How are the children?" Africans have known for some time what Americans are learning: the health of a nation, community, and family depends on the health of children.

> *A survey by The National Commission of Working Women showed that although 93 percent of teenagers say they expect to work as adults, 50 percent of girls and 60 percent of boys said one parent would stay home to raise the kids.*

We should all be alarmed to read studies showing that the majority of juvenile crimes and pregnancies are not conceived in the dark of the night, but from three to six o'clock in the afternoon. With over 71 percent of mothers of school-age children working, there are at least five million children whose parents admit their kids are in "self-care."

Lest I be misunderstood, I am not advocating that mothers not work outside the home. I watched my generation struggle with this dilemma. In the 70s we donned our business pantsuits and even neckties to claim our places in the corporate world. If we didn't "work" in the 80s, we were made to feel that we had abandoned

The Cause. In the 90s corporate women who never had kids were often frustrated, and "Supermoms" verged on nervous breakdowns. Finally, in this new millennium, women care less about what others think and are doing what's right for them and their families. Many women and men work full-time and balance work and home marvelously, devoting needed time and attention to both.

Women and families need to evaluate their employment needs on an individual basis. I tried working full-time temporarily. I felt like I was a lousy mother, lover, wife, nurse, and me. So, I tried staying home for two years to raise babies. When I began to cut Mark's meat at the table, I knew it was time to find a balance. For me, it was part-time work. My sister tried this same approach and learned that she was her best working full-time. Every family needs to be flexible and needs to figure out what works best. Achieving the best results may require changing the plan again if and when needed.

> *The effect of income on life satisfaction seems limited, researchers say. Once people get past the poverty level, money does not play a role in day-to-day happiness.*

I watched families in my childbirth classes sell their five-bedroom, tri-level homes to buy two-bedroom duplexes so Dad could stay home to care for the baby. Conversely, more often I saw early pregnant couples buy a new home with more bedrooms plus an SUV for the car seat. Then, in postpartum class I watched Mom weep because she "had" to go back to work. It seems unjust that often men and women are caught in the double bind of starting a family at the very same time they're expected to climb the career ladder of success.

As I was wresting with this dilemma in my life, I read a quote that drilled home the priority message: "Success is measured by how your child describes you to a friend."

Perhaps success isn't the person who has the most things, but

Success

"To laugh often and love much; to win the respect of intelligent persons and the affection of children; to earn the approbation of honest citizens and endure the betrayal of false friends; to appreciate beauty; to find the best in others; to give of one's self; to leave the world a bit better, whether by a healthy child, a garden patch or a redeemed social condition; to have played and laughed with enthusiasm and sung with exultation; to know even one life has breathed easier because you have lived—this is to have succeeded."

—Ralph Waldo Emerson

the one who needs less.

While we were applying to adopt Mitch, we shopped for a bigger house. I found the perfect one, however, it was over our budgeted amount. I reasoned that I could work closer to full-time so we could afford it. Our realtor gave us sage advice when he posed this question: "Will you own your house, or will it own you?"

We knew the house would own us. We found another perfect house within our budget.

Does your home or "stuff" own you?

Some people lose their health to make more money, then lose their money to restore their health. If you chase money, it may catch you. And if it catches you, you will be its slave forever.

We've all heard adages such as, "Are you making a living or making a life?" And, "Few people on their death beds say they wish they'd have spent more time at the office." The one that struck me most was, "Tombstones don't say, 'She Was #1 in the Region'; they say, 'Beloved Mother, Wife, and Friend.'"

Audrey Hepburn was the spokesperson for UNICEF when she said, "Take care of the small circle around you. When you have succeeded with them, then step out, one small step at a time."

This principle applies to all the priorities on your list, whatever they may be: your spouse, yourself, your faith, your service.

Too often, we are so busy striving, we don't allow ourselves to "arrive." Our happiness, we believe, is dependent on external things. "I'll be happy when I have more stuff, when the kids are happy, when I have a better job...." True happiness does not come from outer, but inner, abundance.

At various phases of our lives, we must step back and reexamine our priorities and how we are living them. I was blessed to work only part-time while raising our kids. One of my favorite words is "homemaker," for what better job could there be in the world than making a home? Our "price" for that was living in a small but lovely three-bedroom ranch home and driving used cars. That's not for everybody, but it was best for us—a simple price we happily paid. When Mitch flew the coop and our nest was empty, that's when my speaking and writing hobby catapulted into a full-time busy career. Suddenly, this stay-at-home-mom was jet-setting across the nation, gone eighty nights a year, which was expected to double fast. The bookings and the books came rolling in, and it was time to decide: I could leave my home office, rent space, and hire several full-time staff members and make a ton more money, or I could keep my office at home next to Mark's, my one employee, my sanity, and my happy marriage. I examined my priorities and life assignments and chose the latter.

Just because we can do something doesn't mean we should.

To this day, I continue to be challenged to make my number-one priority to be keeping my number-one priority my number-one priority.

What's yours?

Your Turn; Your Time for SelfCare

Make a list of what is most important to you, most deserving of your attention. Include all areas of life—family, faith, friends, fitness, finances, community. List them in order of importance. Put a check by the one that is your number-one priority.

Are you satisfied with the time and attention you are devoting to this priority? If not, what specific steps will you take to change that?

What specific action will you take to show your number-one priority that he/she/it is indeed number one?

What of your "stuff," if any, "owns" you? What specific steps will you take to change that?

If you agree with the importance of family suppertime together, what steps will you take to arrange for it? How many times a week?

With you accountability partner: Share your list of priorities. What specific steps did you take this month to "live" your number-one priority? How did that make you feel?

Chapter 10

"We Don't Have Time for This!"

Managing time wisely

We carried the babies into a mammoth C-5 cargo jet, where all but a few seats had been removed. Down the center, a row of twenty-two cardboard boxes, each approximately two feet square, sat side by side. Two to three babies lay in each box. A long strap stretched from one end of the plane, over the boxes, and attached to the other end. A whole new definition of seatbelt safety. Several large metal trashcans stood at each end with food, formula, and supplies for the trip. The few toddlers and older children sat belted in on the long side benches—bewildered orphans strapped inside a flying boxcar. The captain instructed the nine adults to buckle up for takeoff. I sat with Mitchell on my lap in one of the few seats near the cabin. The sound of the engine's roar was nearly deafening. A panic came over me. My heart raced, and my breath stuck in my chest. Although no words were spoken, each escort must have known what the other was thinking. The last plane load of orphans leaving Saigon blew up shortly after takeoff. It was still unclear whether it had been shot down or sabotaged.

Would ours explode too?

My shaking arms gripped Mitchell close to me. He hugged

me back as if to comfort me. The image of the black fiery cloud refueled the terror I felt when I saw the plane crash.

I began to pray as ours taxied down the runway. I knew if we lived through the next five minutes that Mitch and I would make it home to Iowa. To Mark. To my girls. The motion of the plane lulled the infants to near silence. The adults sat statue-like. Only the engine's vengeful roar broke the haunting, threatening stillness.

I felt the plane lift off the ground.

My heart thumped faster. I prayed faster.

Finally, the captain spoke: "We are out of range of the Vietcong. We are safe. We are going home!"

Shouts of gladness and relief filled the plane. I continued to pray, almost laughing, this time in thanksgiving. The weight of fear lifted from my chest and shoulders. I stood Mitchell on my lap to face me. "We're going home, Son."

Immediately, we adults unfastened our seatbelts and hastened to tend to the babies. Several helpers were Air Force personnel. Others were Americans taking advantage of the opportunity to get out of the country fast.

One burly man with huge hands and salt-and-pepper hair leaned over a box and began changing a diaper. He admitted this was his first, which was obvious, and we laughed with him as he did it clumsily.

Someone whispered, "His wife was killed in the crash a few days ago." No wonder his eyes looked so anxious.

By now all one hundred babies were crying simultaneously. The formula was a perfect temperature, just as the worker had planned, and we propped countless bottles to rehydrate the little ones. We quickly learned to feed all three babies in a box at the same time by placing them on their sides and propping their bottles on the shoulders of their box-mates. Some sucked the formula down in only minutes, whereas others needed more help. I cradled a baby girl in my folded legs and coaxed her to drink while using my other hand to feed another baby. The nipple fell from the mouth of the one in my lap. Clearly, she was too weak to suckle. Using both hands, I milked formula from the nipple to her mouth. While other babies protested, I continued until an ounce was taken.

Although it was difficult work, a sense of merriment danced between us volunteers...we were taking children to freedom, to families.

As the bottles emptied, we draped diapers over our shoulders and burped two at a time.

Soon, the predicted diarrhea became a reality, and we changed one diaper after the other. The handsome burly man wrinkled his face as he dangled a dirty mess between his thumb and index finger and took it to the assigned trash can.

With one in my arms and two in my lap, I held and fed three infants at a time. Then I noticed the baby girl with a cleft palate, crying so hard she was hoarse. I picked up the wee one, and she rested limply in my lap. It didn't take a pediatric nurse to diagnose exhaustion and dehydration. Drop by drop, I squeezed formula from the bottle through her deformed lip. The engine thundered, the babies wailed, the walls vibrated, my heart ached, and my stress escalated as I listened to ninety-nine babies protest while I gave undivided attention to one.

After nearly six hours of feeding, burping, and changing babies, we heard the pilot announce we would stop in the Philippines to refuel. That didn't sound unrealistic to our crew, but the news that we would be detained for each baby to have a medical checkup caused complaining.

"We've got to get these babies home," I grumbled. "We don't have time for this."

Time is the only thing every person in the world has the same amount of every day. How we use it is our decision.

How often, when people ask how you are, do you answer, "Busy"? How many times do you find yourself saying, "I don't have the time to eat. I don't have time to exercise. I don't have time to pray. I don't have time for play. I simply don't have time!"

Lack of enough time is said to be the number-one stressor for women. (Men's number one is finances, with lack of time a close second.) How is it possible that with so much technology and so many time-saving devices at our fingertips, we often feel more stressed, more overwhelmed, less in control, and less able to get it all done?

> Mother Teresa feared that, "Children have no time for parents. Parents have no time for each other. In the home begins the disruption of world peace."

Cell phones are, for sure, a mixed blessing. They were supposed to save us time, but most people would agree they rob us of time as well. We are rarely not "on call," at the whim of our ringing phones. It's important to remember that we have control over them, not vise versa. We can turn them off and on at will. We can choose how to use our time.

One day, on an hour-long road trip, I happened to follow a car occupied by a woman and four kids. For the entire sixty miles, the driver talked on her cell phone, and I felt sad for her. My car time was sometimes my best time with my kids. (Maybe because I held them captive and they had no choice.) I loved driving them places because they talked then. But they can't talk to us if we're on the phone.

Recently, I read an article titled "Great News for Time-Strapped Parents." It reported on a kiddie concierge business that would save parents time by arranging play dates for their children, research the best ballet classes and ball teams, and then deliver the children there for them. That didn't sound like great news to me. An adjacent ad suggested that you didn't have to take time to be with your child; you could call him or her on your matching cell phones instead.

Many of us are time-strapped because we work really hard. We spend a lot of our time working and then shopping to acquire possessions... lots and lots of possessions. Feng shui, the ancient Chinese system for creating harmony in our environment, warns against the surplus of material goods. Its first rule is: no clutter. Most faith traditions extol simplicity as a means to spiritual enlightenment. In Roman Catholicism, austerity, exemplified by monks and nuns, has been held for centuries as a model. Buddhism stresses the relationship between external simplicity and internal insight.

> *New things give our brains a hit of the feel-good medicine, dopamine, which is pleasurable but fleeting. Dozens of studies show that many of the things we think will bring us happiness do not— at least not for long. A University of Illinois study proved that no matter how eagerly anticipated something was, within three months its effect on people's well-being was negligible.*

Lifestyle experts and religious leaders describe a growing appreciation by many Americans that an overabundance of goods can be a drag on spiritual development. Increasingly, de-cluttering and downsizing are being viewed in a spiritual context as ways to remove detraction to inner growth. People are realizing that the more they have, the more they have to take responsibility for, leaving less breathing space.

These lessons are important to teach our children too. Remember, we are always role modeling, and we need to show them that we— and they—cannot have it all, so we'd better teach them now.

Life is about choices. They need to choose between gymnastics and soccer and baseball and ballet and music lessons. We've created a "hurried-child" trend in this country by hyper-scheduling our kids. Busyness has become a status symbol. Downtime is seen as anti-American.

Like us, children need space for silence and contemplation for their mental health.

A University of Michigan study found that free time for children under the age of thirteen has fallen 16 percent in a single generation.

Researchers at Rutgers University surveyed one thousand workers around the country, and 95 percent said they are concerned about spending more time with their families. So what is stopping them?

Given a choice, 40 to 60 percent of Americans would take more time instead of more money.

The Families and Work Institute says 33 percent of women and 28 percent of men would prefer to work part-time if they could afford it. They must have figured out that even if you win the rat race, you're still a rat. If you chase money, it may catch you—if it catches you, you'll forever be its slave.

When the typical person is asked if he or she feels more time-poor or money-poor, the answer is almost always time-poor.

Our society places a lot of importance on work. Wouldn't it be great if we placed more importance on time spent playing and having fun? When was the last time you scheduled a "play date" for yourself? Playtime is crucial for grownups too. Hobbies and other fun activities help us sharpen our skills, express creativity, and simply blow off steam, which reduces stress. When we become engrossed in an activity, our brains can get in a near-meditative state, which benefits our bodies, minds, and spirits. Besides, playing brings added joy to our lives—a great way to spend our time.

Tips to Slow Down

1) Leave holes in your daily calendar instead of filling every minute. Easing the pressure on your time allows you to slow down.

2) Monitor your pace. Don't move quickly out of habit.

3) Take a deep breath and consciously slow down.

4) Add ten minutes to every schedule as flex time, allowing for delays.

5) Eat meals slowly, always sitting down at a table. Never stand to eat.

6) Make time for at least one hobby that allows you to slow down.

7) Turn off all technology and noise for a specified time each day. Sit quietly.

8) Drive slower.

9) Do one thing at a time.

10) Breathe.

My time is precious, so I hate to waste it. Some people are penny pinchers; I'm a minute pincher. Are you like me? If it takes twenty minutes to get to an appointment, do you leave exactly twenty minutes before you're to be there? It took many years of New Year's resolutions to discipline myself to leave just five minutes earlier so I'm under less pressure en route. Try it. If you arrive a few minutes early, read from your motivational or inspirational books kept in the car for this sacred time.

It took me too long to realize how I was putting myself under undue pressure. I used to leave a message on my business answering machine saying I would be back by a specific hour to return calls. Then I found myself rushing through snarled traffic or shoving a grocery cart at warp speed so I could meet my own self-imposed deadline! Finally, I learned to say I would be back "mid-afternoon." This tiny change reduced my stress immensely.

Sometimes we waste time by being too busy. These stinging words from Max Lucado reminded me of the danger of that: "Busyness rapes relationships. It substitutes shallow frenzy for deep friendships. It promises satisfying dreams but delivers hollow nightmares. It feeds the ego but fractures a family. It cultivates a program, but plows under priorities."

It's important to slow down. Maybe we need to do less. Burning the candle at both ends results in, well, burnout. Slowing down allows us time to gather and conserve our energy. It allows us to be present to ourselves and others.

We have a lot more control of our time than we exercise.

We can choose to slow down.

We can choose not always to be "busy."

We can choose how to spend our time.

Your Turn; Your Time for SelfCare

Log your time. Buy or create a daily appointment book, and at the end of the day record how you spent each hour. Notice, how did you really spend your time? What one thing do you want to change?

What specific steps will you take to accomplish this change?

This circle represents the twenty-four hours of your day. Section off the amount of time you sleep. (Hopefully, it will be about one-third of the circle—in other words, eight hours. ☺)

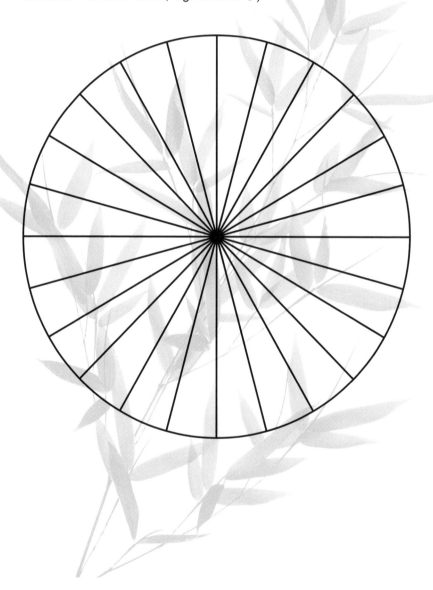

Write in the spaces the time you spend working. Driving. Eating. Exercising. Praying. Playing. Spending time with family. Watching TV. Emailing. Surfing on the Internet. Relaxing. Doing household chores. What else?

How much time are you devoting to your priorities?

With your accountability partner: Study this chart carefully, prayerfully. This is the life you have created. Are there things you'd like to change?

On this circle, divide the sections according to how you want to live your day. Make a copy, post it where you can see it. Visualize it. Change it. It's your life.

What steps will you take to make these changes?

Chapter 11

"What Do I Do Now?"

Making good decisions

The plane made a smooth landing on the runway of Clark Air Force Base. Babies gently bumped against each other as the plane came to a halt.

"Why didn't they just let us get to Oakland as soon as possible, where the babies can get care?" I muttered to another volunteer.

I felt a little selfish when she answered, "Some babies could be in critical condition if they waited until then."

My eagerness to get home had overshadowed my logic.

Looking out the window, I was surprised to see dozens of women on the landing strip, obviously there to help with our mission. One by one they entered the back door of the plane and exited the front, each carrying a baby.

"We're U.S. military wives," a pretty blonde explained as she took an infant from Ross. "We're thrilled to be a part of this," she said, nodding toward the fussing cargo.

Another woman approached me and reached to take Mitchell from my arms.

"Oh, no, you don't," I protested with a laugh.

She smiled politely. "We're under strict instructions to take every baby from the plane. No exceptions, I'm afraid."

I clutched him closer to me. "No. I'm his mom."

She persisted. "Each child must be checked in, according to the government airlift plan."

She reached for him again, and I gently pushed her hand away. "You don't understand what I've been through to get him." My voice broke. "I almost lost him once. Never again."

Carol and Ross came to convince me to let him go. "We escorts are to be taken to a nice motel where we can clean up and rest. Then you'll be with him again," Carol assured me.

"I don't want to go to a nice motel. I want to be with my son," I pouted, then reluctantly handed Mitchell to the stranger.

I kissed him in her arms. "Mommy will be there soon, Honey."

He didn't seem to oppose the separation, but my arms and heart felt empty without him.

Deep down I knew it was probably best. I felt weak, and my cramping was increasing again.

We deplaned and walked across the hot pavement. The air felt fresher and less humid, though as hot as in Saigon. We were ushered into a dimly lit building off the tarmac, where women in American Red Cross uniforms greeted us. Because telephone communication was nearly impossible in Vietnam, their primary purpose was to call our families to let them know of our safe arrival.

One lady in a uniform smiled and said, "I understand this plane load of one hundred babies is just a start—there are more planes and more children coming."

"We have another two hundred babies that should be here tomorrow," Ross said hopefully.

A gray-haired worker added, "The news reported that London sent a Boeing 707 to Saigon for one hundred fifty orphans."

"I heard Australia flew out over two hundred," the lady in

the red vest offered.

"We can vouch for that!" Carol attested. "We were there and put some of our babies on that plane."

"Another sixty-three went to Canada and fifty more to West Germany," another chimed in.

"Wow," I breathed, barely comprehending the magnitude of this adventure.

The lady in the red vest put her arm around my shoulder. "Volunteering to save hundreds of babies was extraordinary."

I smiled meekly. "I volunteered for six."

She seemed startled. "It wasn't your decision from the start to help rescue hundreds?"

I shook my head and chuckled. "I doubt I'd have been brave enough to make that decision."

It's unlikely that you will ever have to decide whether to fly into a warring country. Yet you're faced with decisions, big and little, every day. How do you make them?

Being healthy in mind, body, and spirit is crucial for making good decisions because we can't make good judgments when we feel exhausted physically, mentally, or spiritually. When we are strong, healthy, and whole, we are better equipped to make sound choices.

Here are several less-than-optimal ways we sometimes make decisions, along with recommendations for ways to make them better:

Too often we don't consider what's best for us. The same altruistic qualities that call us to work in healthcare are the same characteristics that allow us to shortchange ourselves. We do what's best for others, sometimes at the cost of what is best for us. It doesn't have to be either or.

When possible, make decisions that benefit others and are healthy for you too.

Often we make decisions on the spur of the moment, under times of stress when adrenaline is pumping. These are not the best circumstances in which to make any decision, big or small. You've likely been in situations like that. You're in a meeting and somebody calls for help with a project, and they call for help, and they call for help again, and you raise your hand, and you are it, and you are in, and you are involved, and you said yes again.

That's how I, a novice, became a 4H leader of thirty kids and 100 horses! As much as I loved it, I was in over my head with too much on my already-over-crowded plate. It took me way too long to learn to never say yes at the moment. Now I try to say (and I suggest you try it too), "Let me think (or pray) about it and I'll call you tomorrow." Let's remind ourselves that if it is a good decision today, it will still be a good decision tomorrow.

Sometimes decisions are made too quickly in the form of misspoken words. In the heat of the moment, words are said in haste, without forethought, without peace, sometimes in anger and frustration, and lives are changed forever.

Instead, count to ten. Bite your tongue. Breathe deeply. Speak carefully.

Good decisions are made in a place of peace. You need to have the time, space, and solitude to make healthy choices. Even ordinary small ones should be made in this way. Try taking deep breaths in a quiet environment to evaluate the facts before you decide. When a decision is big, maybe life-changing, get out of Dodge. Find a quiet place for an overnight stay, unaffected by the stress and turmoil.

It is there, in a place of peace, that good decisions can be made.

In that quiet space, listen to your deep inner voice. Whether you call it intuition, the Holy Spirit, or higher consciousness, remember, that still small voice is your built-in guide, your Divine guidance. It must be listened to, respected, and followed. We cannot hear it in the chaos. Be still. Listen. Follow.

Occasionally we make decisions that are not consistent with our priorities. Don't give lip service to one thing, claiming it is a priority in your life, then make decisions distracting you from that.

Rotary International's Four-Way Test

Of the things we think, say, or do, ask the following four questions:

1) Is it the truth?
2) Is it fair to all concerned?
3) Will it build goodwill and better friendships?
4) Will it be beneficial to all concerned?

Sometimes we make decisions that are not aligned with our values. Wouldn't the world be a better place if we all followed the Rotary Four-Way Test in our business and professional lives?

I try (try, being the operative word here) to make my decisions based on this philosophy: If you make the right decision today, the God you believe in takes care of the rest. While that is simple, it is not always easy. Too often we make decisions that are not right today, but we think they will work out in the long run. Perhaps we twist the numbers just a bit or inflate the resume a little or step on someone on our way up, believing it will all be worthwhile. That never works, not in the end. What a lot of faith it takes, in ourselves and our God, to make the right decision today, based on that deep inner voice and trust that our Creator will take care of the rest.

Early in my speaking and writing career I won a prestigious writing contest run by a major magazine. My prize was the honor of attending a coveted week-long writing retreat, making me a regular contributor for the publication—every new writer's dream. The disappointing news was that I had a speaking engagement contracted smack dab in the middle of that week. The writing seminar was a once-in-a-lifetime opportunity, and I wanted desperately to cancel my engagement or substitute another speaker. But deep down in my gut, I knew it was wrong. So I missed the writing retreat and kept my commitment to my client. And from that event I got another contract worth four times my fee! I made the right decision that day, and God took care of the rest.

This philosophy and practice takes all the pressure off. Make the moral, ethical, deep-down-in-your-gut-you-know-it's-right decision today. It's simple, and with practice it becomes easy.

That leads to the next best way to make good decisions—always tell the truth. Make sure that every word that comes out of your mouth is true. Big or small. If the project takes two weeks, don't say one. If it cost $200, don't say $190. Honesty is indeed the best policy. Remember what Will Rogers said, "Tell the truth. It's a lot easier to remember."

Sometimes people are stuck with decisions they made before they could vote! Would you ask an eighteen-year-old for career advice today? When you decided to pursue your current path, how old were you? I know an electrical engineer who, at age forty, had a revelation: "I really wanted to be an artist!" Because he chose engineering in high school, he felt "stuck" with it the rest of his life.

I loved my life as a nurse and had no interest in changing careers. Yet, when my speaking "hobby" catapulted, I had to make a big decision, to do something else, to change my path and follow a new passion. Is there something else you'll decide to be or do?

To make good decisions, there are times when we need to just say, "No." This is hard for many of us to do since we think we need to be all things to all people. Dear Abby gave me great advice on that in one of her columns. I was relieved to read that I didn't have to give a reason for why I couldn't help. (I thought I had to explain that I was already chairing the church bazaar and collecting money for the cancer drive and managing thirty kids and one hundred horses, so I didn't have time to bake cookies for the third-grade class picnic.) Abby told me I didn't have to give a reason. All I had to do was say, "I'm sorry, I can't; I have another commitment." What a relief! That commitment can be taking care of yourself, your family, your priorities. Try it next time. It may save you from shoveling horse poop!

It's hard to say no, though, when others are pleading and counting on you, isn't it? In those situations, consider this: It's only when you step back that others can step forward. Every time you say, "Yes," it deprives another person of an opportunity. When you decline, it gives that person a chance to serve, to learn, to grow.

Owning a decision is crucial for living with it. Avoid using the words "have to." It's said we don't "have to" do anything but die and pay taxes. I'd submit that we don't "have to" pay taxes. We choose to live in a country that collects taxes, and we can choose to pay them or go to jail.

If making a decision is difficult, do you ever postpone it for an inordinate amount of time? But not to decide is to decide. Even no decision is a decision. Think about it.

Remember, where you are today is based on decisions you made in the past. Where you will be tomorrow is based on decisions you make today. Take the time and exercise the wisdom to make them good ones.

Making better decisions every day makes us better people, and as better people we are recognized and offered better opportunities, which in the end brings better rewards.

Your Time; Your Turn for SelfCare

What is one small decision you make every day that you can make better?

What big decision do you need to make? To make that decision in a place of peace, where will you go? When?

Is there a big decision you need to make, to do something else, to change your path or follow a new passion? Explain here.

Is there a time you wished you'd have said, "I'm sorry, I can't; I have another commitment"? Describe it.

Was there a time you said that this month? How did it make you feel?

In what current or future occasion will you step back so others can step forward?

With your accountability partner: In what current situation will you change from using the words "have to" to "choose to" so you'll feel empowered by making your own decisions and life choices?

Chapter 12

"We Did It! We Made a Difference"

Sticking to life assignments; making a difference

A cool, gentle breeze blew my hair across my sweaty cheek as the open-air bus transported us to the motel. Palm trees and colorful flowers provided a peaceful setting.

But I didn't feel at peace.

Days of caring for all the infants had distracted my fear, but now, in this lull, it resurfaced, too powerful to suppress. *How long will it take to check all the babies? How long will we have to stay here? I won't feel safe again until I'm on U.S. soil.*

The bus dropped us off at the motel, and Ross and I sauntered past a bed of lush exquisite flowers amidst swaying palm trees. I inhaled the fresh, sweet air, trying to breathe in the tranquility. It was no use.

I blurted out, "I know I'm paranoid, Ross, but I still don't feel safe here." Ashamed of my stubborn fear, I went on. "It's suspected that the Vietcong shot down one plane load of orphans. What if they try to bomb these babies here?"

He listened with a straight face. "LeAnn, no country would bomb a U.S. air base as powerful as this."

"I suppose not," I heard myself say.

He patted my back gently. "We're safe here. Really."

"Of course," I said with fake confidence.

I entered our room and plopped onto the floral bedspread while Carol took a shower. The fluffy pillow under my head reminded me that I'd left my sweater at the center. I hoped one of the workers would wear it and remember me.

Ross's words echoed in my head: "We're safe here." Finally, the peace I craved began to ease into my heart and mind.

After I took my turn in a long warm bath, Carol and I met Ross and Sister Terese at the mess hall. The American cuisine tasted great. I declined the salad. We ate together, slowly, quietly. We welcomed the relaxation but admitted to each other an uncomfortable sense of loss and emptiness. Sister Terese knew the cure.

"Let's go see the babies!" she declared.

"And find my son!"

Instantly, we took our trays to the conveyor belt and rushed to the gymnasium. It appeared to be the size of a hanger. Hundreds of single-bed mattresses lay in neat rows, covered with white sheets, with diapers, clothes, and toys stacked on one end. We beamed to see our babies, each with their own bed and caregiver. The many unoccupied mattresses awaited the arrival of more children. Sister Terese burst into tears. "Somebody cares for them," she said, blowing her nose and wiping her eyes. "Somebody besides us cares for them."

After a group hug, I couldn't wait another minute, and we split up to find Mitch.

Nagging fear crept over me as I imagined that somehow he could have been lost. Still amazed by the maternal instinct that bonded me to him, I marched slowly between the rows, rhythmically moving my head from left to right, staring at each baby.

Then, there he was. In the middle of the gym I found him sitting contently in the arms of a volunteer.

"He's my son," I told the curly-haired woman, who looked at me skeptically.

As if to prove it, Mitchell reached for me. Having him back in my arms made me feel complete.

"You're a lucky mama," the woman said. "He is a wonderful baby. The doctor was just here and said he's a healthy one too."

Relieved, I swayed him in my arms.

Ross, Carol, and Sister joined me, and we all listened as the Air Force wives told us how two of our babies had been hospitalized but were expected to do very well. Dehydration and fever were the primary problems, and these wee ones had no reserve.

My friends went back to the motel, but I couldn't leave Mitch. Not yet. We played on the mattress for a while, peek-a-booing and rolling a little ball back and forth. When the lights in the gymnasium dimmed, I sat cross-legged, rocking him in my arms. He nestled his head into my neck and breathed softly as I sang him our family's favorite lullabies. Soon he was asleep, and I gently laid him on his tummy and covered him with a light blanket. I kissed his soft, smooth cheek. "Good night, son." I loved how that sounded.

I tiptoed past the rows and rows of one hundred babies cooing and sleeping on clean, crisp mattresses, being tended by whispering volunteers. For the first time, the immensity of what we had been a part of in Operation Babylift nearly overwhelmed me.

It had been an incredible unexpected life assignment, but we had done it.

We made a difference.

When I first arrived in Vietnam and learned about Operation Babylift and that we'd help bring out not six but three hundred babies, I knew I was somehow on assignment. And I feel I'm still on assignment. We all are. What's yours? What is your purpose? Your mission? What is your Creator's plan for you on Earth?

Sometimes we deliberately and thoughtfully sign up for serving others with our employment or volunteerism. And sometimes we don't sign up at all; it's put upon us, and we may even think or say, "I didn't sign up for this."

It's important to discern which of our life assignments we signed up for and which were assigned to us, because usually it's more difficult to commit our time, energy, resources, and enthusiasm to assignments for which we did not enlist. Yet often they are duties we cannot shirk. This leads us into "war zones," where we must build strength to cope. That's a primary mission of this book.

I speak to thousands of caregivers every year. Many of them are paid professionals who "signed on." Millions are family members who were "assigned to" their tasks. They never expected this appointment, and they may feel ill-equipped and overwhelmed.

I didn't sign up to rescue hundreds of babies in a place where gunshots woke me in the night. My devoted husband didn't sign up for a wife who flew into a war torn country. Like us, you may not see the meaning of it all while you're going through the "war zones" of your lives, but when you stay true to your assignments, you do the right thing, even though it may not be easy or even make sense at the time, you will look back and discover the purpose, the lesson... yes, even the goodness... of it all.

And it is then you will realize the difference you made.

And what a difference you make as a part of the healthcare team, whether you're pushing papers or brooms or pills.

I've noticed that people who are called to serve in healthcare are those who usually serve in other areas too. They have the hearts of caregivers in their personal and professional lives. They are often volunteers in their schools, communities, churches, and even world missions.

Many employers encourage their staff to tithe and/or do community service. They know it not only benefits the community, but the employee. Giving makes people feel powerful, and employers are attracted to that. The end result is increased success for the employee and the employer. How did you feel the last time you gave of your money or service? You projected those feelings, and others noticed. Everyone won.

I personally am a big believer in tithing, which includes donations made not only to religious institutions but contributions to all charitable causes. Tithing isn't only giving of our treasures but giving of our time and talents. We can give by teaching someone to read, shoveling a neighbor's sidewalk, phoning a shut-in, or sending a get well card. No effort is too small.

> *"This is what we are all about. We plant the seeds that one day will grow. We water seeds already planted, knowing they hold future promise. We lay foundations that will need further development. We provide yeast that produces effects far beyond our capabilities. We cannot do everything, and there is a sense of liberation in realizing that. This enables us to do something and do it very well. It may be incomplete, but it is a beginning, a step along the way, an opportunity for the Lord's grace to enter and do the rest."*
> *—Archbishop Oscar Romero*

Many of us struggle to find the balance between no involvement and over involvement. It helps to realize we do not have to do it all.

Remember the Bible story of the little boy who donated his few loaves of bread and fishes, and Jesus then turned them into enough food to feed thousands? Notice that He did not ask the boy to organize the fishermen or create unions for bread bakers. He asked him to give what he had. Like us.

I was right when, as a kid trick or treating for UNICEF, I determined we are called to be our brothers' keepers. We can all make a difference.

> *"Do unto others as you would have them do unto you."*
> —*Christianity*

Traditional Jews believe that when we leave this world it ought to be a better place than when we entered it. The concept is known as Tikkun Olam, which means "Repair of the World" or, in other words, making the world a better place for all living things.

> *"Hurt not others in ways that you yourself would find hurtful."*
> —*Buddhism*

> *"What is hateful to you, do not to your fellow man."*
> —*Judaism*

There are more than 1,100,000 nonprofit organizations in the United States alone. How marvelous that we gather as citizens, using the power of our freedom, to serve others. Still, the needs can seem overwhelming. On those days we ponder how miniscule our contributions are in the scope of things, and we wonder, is my small part really worth it?

> *"No one of you is a believer until he desires for his brother that which he desires for himself."*
> —*Islam*

> *"Blessed is he who preferred his brother before himself."*
> —*Baba'i Faith*

Indeed it is! Remember, no effort is too small. Everything you do matters far more than you know and has ramifications far beyond your knowledge

> *"Do not do to others what you would not have them do to you."*
> —*Confucianism*

2.5 million children in the world die every year for lack of diarrhea medicine.

or expectations. You may not be called to rescue babies in cardboard boxes in a Third-World country, but you rescue people every day by serving.

Mother Teresa, my hero, said it best: "I cannot do great things. I can only do small things, with great love."

Like you.

Your Turn; Your Time for SelfCare

What are your current life assignments, your mission, your Creator's plan for you on earth? To determine your assignments, begin by making a list of all the activities that consume your time. At home. At work. In the community.

As you review your list, circle those things:
you are good at
you love doing
that make a difference.

Likely, these chores are some of your life assignments. These are areas that utilize your giftedness and fulfill you while bringing goodness to the world.

Next, examine whether your assignments are congruent with your priorities and your values. If they are not, cross them off your list.

Which of your circled activities did you sign up for?

Which were assigned to you?

How did you feel the last time you gave of your money or service?

With your accountability partner: When was a time you saw the direct results of your efforts and could see what a difference you had made?

Finding Peace in Your "War Zone"

"I've never seen so many lights or so much activity here," the pilot announced as we circled the airport in Iowa. "There must be a celebrity on this flight."

I turned around, trying to look nonchalant as I gazed at the passengers and wondered who that might be. I didn't recognize anyone famous.

When the plane landed and came to a stop, my heart thumped rapidly as I stood with Mitchell in my arms. The attendant reminded me that it was cool in Cedar Rapids and gave me a blue flight blanket to put around him.

I descended the stairs, and when my feet touched the runway, I was tempted

to sprint into the building and Mark's arms. When I'd called him from our layover, I had my speech rehearsed to tell him about Mitch. But before I could speak, he said through tears, "Just tell me you have our son."

It took all the restraint I could muster to walk slowly into the building. But I couldn't see. Bright lights glared in my eyes. Confused, I stopped for a moment to try to grasp what was happening. Cameras flashed. Reporters shouted questions.

I inched my way forward through the blinding glare. Mark stepped through the lights with open arms, his smile shining across his face.

I eased into his embrace and held him tightly. More than once in Saigon I had feared I would never again feel this touch. I couldn't let go as I felt his arms wrapping around me and our son.

The joy was overwhelming.

This was all I needed in the world.

My life was complete.

I stepped back so Mark could see Mitchell, who opened his arms and reached for his daddy. Mark's eyes brimmed with tears as he drew him to his heart.

Past him, I saw my mom and sisters, Mary and Theresa, there to support me, just as they had done all my life. Having anticipated this media madness, my sister Diane stayed home with our daughters. I felt confused, like I was dreaming when I hugged them and other relatives who had come to meet the plane.

My mind was a whirlwind.

Mark seemed to be directing me down a corridor away from the crowds and press. "You're going to have to trust me on this one, Honey," he said. "You're going to hold a

press conference."

I couldn't believe my ears.

"Mark, I can't. I don't want to. I only want to go home."

"You have no idea what's been going on here since you've been gone. The newspapers and TV reporters have been calling day and night. This is the biggest story that's happened in a long time. They all promised that if you talk to them now, they'll leave us alone."

By that time we were entering a large room filled with reporters. Microphones cluttered the long table in front.

Everything was happening so fast.

I wanted desperately to turn and leave but trusted Mark

absolutely.

I stifled a laugh as I sat down in front of all those mikes and all those people. It seemed like something you would see on *Meet the Press*, not something I should be doing. Mark and I took turns holding Mitchell as the questions were fired. Mitchell smiled and patted his hands and waved at the lights.

Finally, Mark said that was enough and ended the session. Still, persistent reporters called out questions and attempted to follow us to the parking lot. Mark turned and reminded them firmly of the deal that had been made, and they retreated as we made our way to the car.

"I can't wait to go home with you," I said softly as I hugged Mark again before getting in.

"We're not going home," he apologized. He knew I'd be disappointed. "We're going to your mom's." He explained the badgering he had experienced from the reporters the past few days. He didn't trust them to honor the agreement to respect our privacy.

I was indeed disappointed. This was not at all how I had envisioned our homecoming. Yet going to Mom's, where I'd be nurtured and surrounded by my big loving family, did sound appealing.

During the thirty-minute ride to Vinton, alone with Mark and Mitchell, I felt carefree. There was so much we both wanted to say, but we hardly knew where to begin. Mostly, I just wanted to hear all about him and the girls. No one had told Angela and Christie I was bringing Mitchell home. Mark thought it would be wonderful to tell them in person because they loved "surprises." I knew they'd be asleep at Diane's since it was nearly midnight, but I wanted to go just to see them, not wake them.

Until I entered Mom's house.

Something inside me clicked off. The stress that had provided the energy to keep going was suddenly gone. Exhaustion immobilized me. It didn't take much to convince me I should wait until morning to see our girls.

We made Mitchell a mattress of blankets on the floor next to our bed in the guest room. Mom apologized for the poor accommodations for him on short notice. I laughed as I tried to explain how he slept on mats on floors throughout this trip and began to tell them about the center in Saigon with scores of babies.

A part of me wanted to stay up all night and talk endlessly about all that had happened. I knew they would have listened if my fatigue had not made it impossible.

After hugging Mom and thanking her for being there for us, I shut off the light and slipped into bed with Mark. I felt the strong, safe embrace of love I had longed for so often in the past ten days. It was then that the tears I had suppressed throughout this incredible day poured out.

I was up several times in the night with stomachaches and diarrhea but still managed to sleep until the late hour of nine o'clock, when I heard Angela's and Christie's voices. I snuck out of bed, tiptoed past our sleeping son, and rushed to the living room.

"Hi, Mommy!" Angela and Christie chimed as their pigtails bobbed. I stooped to hug them both at the same time. I laughed to keep from crying as they bounced into my arms. I pretended to fall backward onto the floor as they smothered me with kisses. How wonderful to feel their chubby little arms around me as we rolled on the floor in joy!

Then there he was.

Mitch had crawled from the bedroom to the doorway. Before I could speak any words of explanation, he crept into my lap with the girls. They gasped. Angela beamed at me and said, "This must be my brother!"

Someone once said happiness is a choice. Although that is likely oversimplified, it is still true. You have the power to choose and create a happy healthy life. It takes as much effort to live an unrewarding life as it does to lead a rewarding, joy-filled one. It depends on your choices.

The life lessons I've shared in this book are basic. The tools are simple (though not always easy to implement). Deep down, do you believe in them? Then, do them. Watch the positive results unfold.

You can balance your life physically, mentally, and spiritually; you can make healthy good decisions; you can truly live your priorities; and when you do, you are in a better place to make an even bigger difference in this world.

Gandhi said, "We must become the change we seek in the world."

Change.

You can do this.

You deserve it.

Now, embrace all you love, and with peace in your heart, go roll on the floor in joy!

The End

Notes and Stuff I Want to Do or Remember

Notes and Stuff I Want to Do or Remember

Notes and Stuff I Want to Do or Remember

Notes and Stuff I Want to Do or Remember

Notes and Stuff I Want to Do or Remember

Ending Survey 2

"Your Personal SelfCare Survey"

Congratulations of completing your SelfCare for HealthCare program. I hope by now the changes in your health and happiness are evident. This survey will show you the progress you have made (and reveal areas that you can continue to work on.) SelfCare is a lifelong process. Continue, and enjoy, the journey!

1) My original hopes and goals for working in healthcare are still being fulfilled now.

     5 Always

     4 Very often

     3 Fairly often

     2 Sometimes

     1 Rarely. I'm rehearsing, "Do you want fries with that?"

2) I'm coping well with the "war zones" (challenges) of my life.

     5 Always

     4 Very often

     3 Fairly often

     2 Sometimes

     1 Rarely... Not only am I not coping in my "war zones," I need a helmet!

3) I identify stressors in my life and utilize healthy strategies for managing stress.

    5 Always

    4 Very often

    3 Fairly often

    2 Sometimes

    1 Burning out here!

4) I eat 3 healthy meals a day in appropriate quantities.

    5 Always

    4 Very often

    3 Fairly often

    2 Sometimes

    1 Hello #3 Value Meal!

5) I drink 5-6 glasses of water a day.

    5 Always

    4 Very often

    3 Fairly often

    2 Sometimes (so what am I, a camel?)

    1 Spittin' cotton

6) I get 7-8 hours of sleep in a 24 hour period.

    5 Always

    4 Very often

    3 Fairly often

    2 Sometimes

    1 Huh? Sorry I dosed off.

7) I exercise, even briefly, 5 days per week.

    5 Always

    4 Very often

    3 Fairly often

    2 Sometimes

    1 Somebody bring me the remote.

8) I breathe slow and deep 3-4 times per day, as well as in times of stress.

    5 Always

    4 Very often

    3 Fairly often

    2 Sometimes...Did you say yoga? I thought your said Yogi, as in bear.

    1 Rarely

9) I take at least 15 minute daily for relaxation.

    5 Always

    4 Very often

    3 Fairly often

    2 Sometimes ...Are you kidding me? I can barely find time to brush my teeth.

    1 Rarely...I don't floss either.

10) I laugh often and freely throughout the day.

    5 Always... Tears trickle down my pant leg!

    4 Very often

    3 Fairly often

    2 Sometimes

    1 Rarely

11) I spend time with positive, fun-loving people.

    5 Always

    4 Very often

    3 Fairly often

    2 Sometimes

    1 They're suckin' the joy right out of me!

12) I repeat positive affirmations throughout the day.

    5 Always... I am happy and hardly ever complain.

    4 Very often

    3 Fairly often

    2 Sometimes

    1 Rarely

13) I forgive people who have hurt me and I don't hold grudges.

    5 Always

    4 Very often

    3 Fairly often

    2 Sometimes

    1 I'm still mad at dead people!

14) I spend at least 15 minutes a day in quiet meditation, reflection and/or prayer.

    5 Always

    4 Very often

    3 Fairly often

    2 Sometimes

    1 Rarely... My addiction to Facebook takes all my free time.

15) I do a good job of truly living my priorities.

    5 Always... All the glass and rubber balls I'm juggling are most always in the air.

    4 Very Often

    3 Fairly often

    2 Sometimes

    1 Rarely

16) I'm satisfied with the balance between my work and home life.

    5 Completely satisfied

    4 Very satisfied

    3 Satisfied

    2 Somewhat dissatisfied

    1 Who is what's-her-name and does she live here?

17) I manage my time wisely throughout the day to accomplish my goals, balance my life, and live my priorities.

    5 Always

    4 Very often

    3 Fairly often... set the stop watch!

    2 Sometimes

    1 Rarely

18) I make good decisions, big and little.

    5 Always

    4 Very often

    3 Fairly often

    2 Sometimes... I just can't decide if I should decide.

    1 Rarely

19) I feel I'm making a good difference in the world.
>   5 Completely satisfied
>   4 Very satisfied
>   3 Satisfied
>   2 Somewhat dissatisfied
>   1 Very dissatisfied. Not only am I not lighting my candle, it's burning out!

20) I have the power to choose a happier, healthier, rewarding life.
>   5 Always...It's up to me.
>   4 Very often
>   3 Fairly often
>   2 Sometimes
>   1 Rarely

Total points: _____

84-100 Well balanced, happy and healthy. Good job!

68-83   Mostly happy and healthy. Good for you! Continue working on a few specific areas.

52-67   Moderately unhappy and/or healthy. Keep trying. Review areas of lowest scores and repeat those chapter lessons.

36-51   Very unhappy and unhealthy. Start your SelfCare for HealthCare program again and seek other support to make needed changes. You deserve to be happy and healthy.

20-36   Hanging on by a thread! It's time to get some professional help in areas of need. You deserve health and happiness.

About the Author

LeAnn Thieman is a nationally acclaimed Hall of Fame speaker, author, and nurse who was "accidentally" caught up in the Vietnam Orphan Airlift in 1975. Her book, *This Must Be My Brother*, details her daring adventure of helping to rescue 300 babies as Saigon was falling to the Communists. An ordinary person, she struggled through extraordinary circumstances and found the courage to succeed. LeAnn has been featured in *Newsweek Magazine's Voices of the Century* issue, FOX-TV, BBC, NPR, PBS, PAX-TV's It's a Miracle, and countless radio and TV programs.

As a renowned motivational speaker, she shares life-changing lessons learned from her Airlift and nursing experiences. Believing we all have individual "war zones," LeAnn inspires audiences to balance their lives, truly live their priorities and make a difference in the world. An expert in nurse recruitment and retention, she helps organizations care for, hire and inspire their nurses and caregiving team members.

LeAnn is one of about ten-percent of speakers worldwide to have earned the Certified Speaking Professional Designation. In 2008 she was inducted into the Speaker Hall of Fame.

She and Mark, her husband of forty-two years, reside in Colorado where they enjoy their "empty nest."

For more information about LeAnn's books, CDs and DVDs or to schedule her for a presentation and/or SelfCare for HealthCare™ Program, please contact her at:

LeAnn Thieman, LPN, CSP, CPAE
6600 Thompson Drive, Fort Collins, CO 80526
1-970-223-1574   email: LeAnn@LeAnnThieman.com
www.LeAnnThieman.com
www.NurseRecruitmentandRetention.com

More Books By LeAnn

This Must Be My Brother
Adrift in the Storms
Balancing Life in Your "War Zones;" a
Guide to Physical, Mental and Spiritual Health
Chicken Soup for the Nurse's Soul
Chicken Soup for the Nurse's Soul, Second Dose
Chicken Soup for the Christian Woman's Soul
Chicken Soup for the Caregiver's Soul
Chicken Soup for the Father and Daughter Soul
Chicken Soup for the Grandma's Soul
Chicken Soup for the Mother and Son Soul
Chicken Soup for the Christian Soul 2
Chicken Soup for the Adopted Soul
Chicken Soup for the Soul, Living Catholic Faith
Chicken Soup for the Soul, A Book of Miracles
Chicken Soup for the Soul, Answered Prayers